CW00972460

MALEFICE

This Book
Belongs to

Carmen
Glägl

CYCLAMEN © Gay Corran 1986

LESLIE WILSON

Malefice

PICADOR ORIGINAL
PUBLISHED BY PAN BOOKS

First published 1992 by Pan Books Limited

A division of Pan Macmillan Publishers Limited
Cavaye Place London SW10 9PG
and Basingstoke

Associated companies throughout the world

ISBN 0 330 324276

1 3 5 7 9 8 6 4 2

A CIP catalogue record for this book is available from
the British Library

Typeset by Cambridge Composing (UK) Ltd, Cambridge

Printed in Great Britain by
Billing and Sons Ltd, Worcester

For Patricia and Daverick
with thanks

Be it enacted . . . that if any person or persons . . . shall use, practise, or exercise any invocation or conjuration, of any evil or wicked spirit, or shall consult, covenant with, entertain, employ, feed or reward any evil or wicked spirit to or for any intent or purpose, or . . . take up any dead man, woman or child, out of his, her, or their grave, or any other place where the dead body resteth, or the skin, bone, or any other part of any dead person, to be employed or used in any manner of witchcraft, sorcery, charm, or enchantment: or . . . shall use, practise, or exercise any witchcraft, enchantment, charm, or sorcery, whereby any person shall be killed, destroyed, wasted, consumed, pined or lamed in his or her body, or any part thereof . . . every such offender or offenders, their aides, abettors, and counsellors, being of any of the said offences duly and lawfully convicted . . . shall suffer pains of death as a felon or felons . . .

WITCHCRAFT ACT, 1604

I

THE INHERITOR

MARGARET

THEY'RE afraid we'll be found out, my husband and son both. Their arms are slack with fear – so I have to work the harder. I'm not afraid of anyone coming, not now. I shivered for fear while we digged her up, near the gallows where they'd shovelled her away. They'd have hanged us for witches too if they'd found us digging at the gallows.

Mother fetched a hanged man's skull herself one night, she kept it in her cottage. There was moss growing on it, like hair on the poor bald bone – she'd rip it off for her potions, moss from a hanged man's skull, that's powerful. The skull had to put up with everything. No choice. Nor have you any choice, Mother. You're going in with Bridget, so you can sort out your differences. Underground.

They jump to hear me laugh at that, stare at me, angry with me for making a sound. 'Vicar forbade it?' I say to them. 'If he comes, I'll spit in his face.' That frightens them still more – I didn't know they could be scared worse. Are they wondering about me, my son Abe, my husband Thomas? Witchcraft runs in families, they say. Be as virtuous as you like when you're young, it'll catch up with you as you get older.

Hard work, even digging into ground that's been turned before. Flints stop the spade, and the clay's heavy. Last night – after the hanging – we couldn't have done it, not in frozen hard earth. Tonight might have been chosen

3

for us. Last night's moon is hooded like a dark lantern, and the ground is soft and moist, it smells sweet, of spring. Since we have to leave the village, it's a hopeful season to go.

I tell them: 'I'll finish the job alone if you run for it.' My hair's wet, in my eyes, curling out of control as usual. My hair, the only pretty thing about me. Ugly daughter of an ill-favoured mother. And fat! Big Margaret, fit to shift an ox.

Even the labour and sweat don't stop me wondering and thinking, while she lies huddled, waiting to go under the earth. She lay silent while I washed her, while I told her about herself: 'Your breasts are flat, Mother, you hag, your face is black and puffy, your belly is like an old done seedcase – what made you think you were special?' Her glassy eyes gaped up at me. She couldn't even twitch in protest. 'I'm your good daughter, Mother. I'm putting you where you belong, where you'll rest. To give you sound sleep, I'll drop the first stone on your grave, so you can't walk.'

I'm going far away from your laughter, from your wicked tongue, leaving your land, your house, your bits of unspeakable belongings, your malice. To a place where no one knows me or remembers you. You ran once, then came back. I'll never come back. And they'll know where you are, when they find the stones, one from me, one from Thomas, one from Abe. They won't tell Vicar, they won't disturb you. They'll drop more stones. You're caught in holy ground for ever, Mother, with your wrung neck.

I had to wash the shit off her legs. And the piss that spurted out while she throttled. It was hard for her to die. And though my tongue was harsh, my hands were kind – I washed her carcass as if she was one of my own babies. When we leave her down there and cover her up, something of me will stay with her.

Or will I have something of her with me for ever? And what I'm afraid of, is it something that's happened already? Will it, as I try to go forward, pull me over backwards?

CHAPTER ONE

THERE gave Evidence against this Woman, one Alice
Slade by name:

First, the Vicar of the Parish of Whitchurch St Leonard,
where she dwelt; the same later brought the Witch to
confession (though before the Tryal, she had most Stub-
bornly Resisted). And did testify that his Wife (he having
offended the Witch by Urging her to come to Church)
did, two days after being brought to bed of a fair Boy
Child, fall into an Apoplexy, whereof she dyed, and the
Boy would take no Other's milk, and did Dye with his
Mother. And when Asked what she had to say to this
Accusation, the said Alice Slade could speak no Word.

Second, one Martin Tidbury, whose Mother took a
Swarm of Bees, Alice then claiming the bees were her
own Swarm, Sarah Tidbury did Refuse to permit the said
Alice to take them, then was the said Sarah mysteriously
Lamed, and to this day can move neither Arm, nor Leg,
nor Foot on the one side of her, nor that side of her Face,
and was totally Crippled. And the Witch spoke no Word.

Third, there came one Judith Tegg, a neighbour of
the same Alice, an industrious Woman and of good Repute
in the village, who had refused the said Alice the Loan
of Yeaste to make Beere, and the same day did all her
Butter, which she had Prepared for Market, stink most
Foully, and then did her Daughter's hands most horribly
turn Palmside uppermost, and did Judith then call her

Neighbours together and take them to the Witch's House, which done, they cast Alice Slade to the Floore, and did cause the Child to scratch the Witch's cheek (as it is known this mends Hurts caused by a Witch) and when she drew Blood, then did Alice cry most Grievously, and the Child had her Hands restored.

There came Fourthly one Simon Sharpe, a man Lamed in the Wars, earning his Living as a Ratcatcher and Molecatcher, and did Testify how one Night the Witch's Blacke Dogge did Appear unto him, the Witch considering herself Offended by some Words he did Speak to her, and did the same Dogge most sorely Tease and Afflict him, with his Eyes as red as Coals, and did Pursue him about the Lanes, so was the said Simon in Terror for his Life, and the Witch spoke no Word, but the said Simon falling to Railing against the Lord Judge, he was Removed, but was not Punished, since Intercession was made for him, his Wits having been affected in the Wars.

And there came Fifthly one Bridget Tarry, and this was the most Grievous Testimony of all, who had been Robbed, at one Stroke, of Children and Livestock, and was to be Robbed of her very Life, being the Niece and adopted Daughter of the Witch, and testified how from her Childhood she had seen the said Alice engaging in Evil, and had known her to be a most Maleficent woman, and had many times tried to wean her from her Evill, but was repaid with Scorn, how she did marry with the Churchwarden, yet did not weary of Trying to win the Witch for God, but to no Avail, and the Witch stood silent while this testimony was given against her. Then did Bridget testify that she grew fearful, at last, to let the Witch hold her Child, and did Alice Slade turn on her Niece, and say: You only prosper with my Leave. Then did Bridget reply: I want no Prosperity from the Devill. Then did the next day all her chickens die, the Beere sour, the Butter stinke, the spinning Wheel break, and the Cattell fall Dead in their Tracks, likewise the Ox, but worst of all, the Children, one by one, did suffer Convulsions and Die in them. And did the same Bridget run to Alice's house, and pull a piece of Thatch from the Roofe, and did set Light to it, and the Witch did come running, as Witches must when this is Done, and seeing one child Dead, and the other two Dying, did say: Jesus, I never Intended this. Which was taken as Proof against her. And having given Testimony, the said Bridget did fall Stone-Dead as she left the Stand, and the Witch wailed for Fear, for all in the Assize Court would like to Tear her Apart, but the Judge ordered the Court cleared, and said the Witch should dye by process of Execution and no Other.

Then did it seem scarcely Necessary for any other to testify, but there came a sad young Widow, her Babe in her Arms, and did say how the Babe had never seen its Father, for working as Serving Man in the household of Sir Thomas Pollett Justice of the Peace, he was Instructed to turn the Witch Alice away when she did come hawking Honey, and the same Evening did a beam fall on his Head, and he was Instantly Killed. And the Witch spoke no Word. And by this may you tell a Witch, that she can make no Reply to her Accusers.

Then did the Judge find her Guilty of all that was Alleged against her, and especially because of the Instance he had himself Witnessed, and did command that she should be most Expeditiously Hanged, and that she should be kept Close till then, and only a Ghostly Counsellor come Neare her, and the Vicar, Richard Berkeley, did most Christianlike say hee would attempt to Reason with her.

CHAPTER TWO

RICHARD

So HATEFUL she began, so loathly, jeering at me, even
with her end in sight! Yet every hour I was with her, I
saw a change. I was the Vicar of her parish, her soul's
shepherd. She was lost. How could I regret the depriva-
tion of food and sleep – which I suffered with her – when
it is thus that God enters us, when we are broken? I kept
her standing in chains, to her great discomfort. Is the soul
not of more worth than any body? And that she who so
foully abused me when I urged her to go to church, who
so vilely injured me, who lost me my son, my only son,
and taunted me with it, that she should finally look on me
as her only friend – how could I fail to see God's work on
earth most plain and manifest? And surely there is none so
sinful as to be beyond redemption?

It was easy, at first, to defy the clergyman.
  'Did you not know more than you should about
everyone in the village? Where did you come by that
knowledge? You would stand there, telling everyone's
private business to your bees – who were your evil
familiars – what were you plotting with them?'
  He thought: My voice is uncertain, where's my authority? All the time I have lived in this parish I have been
some kind of laughing stock. And this cell stinks. How
shall I bear it?

'You should have come to listen, Richard Berkeley—'
She wagged her matted white head at him.

'You will call me Sir.'

'I will not. You should have come to listen, if you
wanted the truth so much. I might have told you who
was the father of your son.'

She thought: Now he will attack me, and I won't be
able to protect myself. But it was he who cowered, and
put his hand to his mouth. She thought: That made him
smart.

Water dripped in rhythm from the ceiling, measuring
out the remnant of her life. She managed to scratch a flea-
bite. She could see fear on his face.

'Alice Slade, Satan speaks through you still. Has he
promised you he will save you? He will not.'

He was trembling. He thought: What has the Devil told
her about my wife?

'I'll save myself.' She laughed wildly in his face. 'I'll fly
away like the birds, straight through the noose. They
taught me how, when they came to me. When I called
them in their own language.'

She felt the cold trusting feet on her arm and hand, saw
the bright fans of feathers against the sun, heard the
answering whistles and chirps. She thought: The birds
weren't afraid to eat what I offered them. The birds can
fly away from Richard Berkeley.

'There will be no flight, Alice.' But it was as if he were
babbling nonsense, as if it was she who knew the truth.
His voice was a quavering weapon to pit against her tough
old will. 'It will be a long, slow, tormented death. You
will struggle and choke. Then you will have to face the
Lord your God. What will you say to him?'

'I'll ask him why he made the hair fall out of bald fools'
empty heads. And when I'm going to get something to
eat. And a soft feather-bed to sleep in, too.'

She wanted to lie down on the straw: she hated him for keeping her upright.

He reminded himself: I have a chair, while she must stand, or hang uncomfortably by her chains. I will wear her out.

She said: 'It's strange, if I was born to be hanged, why have I always had bad dreams about drowning?'

MARGARET

AND ALL the food I brought my mother in jail, God knows what happened to it. Because I know now he wouldn't give it to her, they told me after the hanging. He had her chained so she could neither sit nor lie down, and once or twice he had the jailers come, take the irons off her, and run her up and down the cell till her head spun.

I raged to think of him denying her sleep, starving her, arguing the wickedness out of her. Why should he be the one to subdue her? I'd always wanted to do it myself.

RICHARD

BETWEEN midnight and two in the morning, much crowds in on me that I cannot escape. When I am unable to sleep, I pick up pen and paper to write it all down, as if this could relieve my soul of its sins. Then I burn it. I have earned little dignity as Vicar of this parish, yet desire to husband the scraps that remain in me: my waking thoughts must not meet the despair of the night before. The paper is fragile, and is gone in seconds.

The rushlights tremble in the draught, dip low to it, all but succumb, but then fire up again in hope. I write thus:

First: I did not, that night, investigate the noises from the churchyard. I knew what was happening there, as must anyone have done who lives nearby. The village has its own intractable idea of what is fitting, and once again I have been defeated. Evil though she was, her body belongs in the churchyard. That is what they think. I am a weak man.

Second: being weak, I am in part to blame for the deaths of my wife and my son. Alice was the instrument, oh yes. I have read all the authorities. I know now how this thing functions. No witch's power is so great that she can prevail against a strong fortress of God.

(I am right to burn this paper, could not this be called the Popish practice of confession? Yet to whom can I confess my sins?)

Third (but less than what is to come): I played chess on a Sabbath night, thinking no evil would come of it. For worldly delight, ignoring the voice of my conscience, advancing the feeble argument that my friend – as I thought him – would return to Oxford the next day, deluding myself that I had a right to a pleasure so long denied me. I *have* no right to pleasure. As I have been shown.

Oh, Susan, such a gentle wife to me, so candid, so different from the rest of your sex – or so much better at deceit. Which do I believe? I wanted your death, or mine, to escape from the torment of uncertainty – and when I saw you stricken by Alice's wickedness, saw you froth at the mouth and your eyes swivel in your head, even then I could not wish it had been I.

Fourth: I doubted my wife's virtue and desired her death. Worse, in so doing, did I not desire damnation, or am I not lost already, is Calvin right, is the soul indeed predestined for heaven or the flames from the moment of birth, is it true that nothing can change this?

No, get thee behind me, Satan. I see you now. Greedy for my soul, as you lusted after the witch's. Have I not despoiled you of Alice Slade?

Fifth, then: I cannot banish Satan when he appears to taunt me. Once I threw my inkpot at him, as Luther did, yet it seems Luther's ink was more powerful than mine, having been (as I am not) a fearless man of courage and fighter for truth. To which he was loyal.

To banish Satan, my conscience tells me, I must be willing to suffer. Yet suffering comes willy-nilly. Oh, God, my son, my only son! Six daughters are left me, each one endangered by Eve's curse.

Tomorrow I will plant a second yew sapling, the other side of the churchyard gate. I will leave two trees behind me, as well as my bones in the churchyard. They will grow through hundreds of years, my answer to weariness and despair. Parson Berkeley's trees, they will call them. If I cannot make them listen to my sermons, the trees will force them to take notice.

I will set it down that Satan is poking his face at me through the bed-curtains – which I see now are infested with moth. His name, thus written down and burned, may speed him back to hell in the morning. He watches me, smiling, pulling his beard, and the sparks jump out from between his long bloody-nailed fingers. He could write a fifth heading on this paper, that which I am determined to forget—

I am falling apart, and the rats scuttle out of their holes to scavenge the pieces. The villagers, farting and snoring through my sermons, never see this, but the assessors who sit high in the gallery of my mind, note Fragmentation against my name. Yet let them write this to my credit: I got a confession out of Alice.

'And what feeble and impotent spite,' sneers Satan, 'made you deny her burial in the churchyard?'

This taunt, too, I will presently burn.

Finally: I am a turncoat, a renegade – this is no secret. To keep my parish, I licked Cromwell's boots, for the sake, I told myself, of my wife and children. Another sin of weakness. And when the King was done to death, I said I was sick of the fever, so no one would remember me preaching on his murder. I am a coward. Bald, spindle-shanked, restless at night, and lame. How could any woman have loved me? It is my curse, that I may not enjoy what I have.

Dear Lord Christ, I would not be these things. Yet could never assume the man I am not, neither with my wife, nor with Alice. Still, let this be set to my credit. I helped save Alice's soul. Or she would have lived on – would she not? – growing wickeder with every year that passed. I was her friend, and, at the last, her master. This must be true. She was not – I will not admit it – stronger than the Church.

––––––––––

'DID YOU not hag-ride your husband to hell? We all knew, do not try to deny it! Day after day he was so worn he could hardly stand on his feet, and when he died, no one believed your mourning.'

'If you drank the amount he was given to drinking, you'd have been in the same state. If I wanted a horse, I'd get myself one that was fit to run. Why do you think I didn't choose you? Neither you nor my husband could have carried me where I wanted to go. And why should I have mourned Francis Slade? He was nothing but trouble and sorrow to me. And if all the work he ever did added up to a day's worth, it's a miracle.'

He thought: I am losing my balance. There is some answer I need to give. I cannot reach it. But he slid on:

'Did you not keep a black dog that came straight from hell? Did you not suckle it at night, and send it to do mischief to your neighbours?'

He knew he was going too fast. It was like that on the ice, he thought, my legs bent away from each other, I had no control any more – no! She's hungry, he thought, and she will be hungrier. I'll have them run her, by and by. I have time, and all the powers I need. I *will* get deeper. His thoughts rang hollow in his head. He thought: Empty. She said my head is empty. It hurts.

'Oh, yes,' she said. 'The black dog. They murdered it because they didn't like its pelt. Poor beast. I chased it away at first, I didn't want another mouth to feed, it was hard enough to keep myself alive.' She let out something between a sigh and a whine. 'It was a cold day, and a colder night, and the creature wouldn't go away. I did shut it out. It cried outside the door. So I let it in. It licked my hand. It was on my side. If they were afraid of it, that was their punishment.' She grinned. 'It pissed on your leg.'

He put a hand to the back of his scalp.

'Hairless fool,' she said. 'I could have saved some of that hair, if you'd asked me. And eased your stiff leg.'

She thought: I shan't speak to him any more. She shut her mouth tight, then opened it again, because her clenched lips made her last teeth wobble, and she thought she wanted to die with some teeth left in her mouth.

She could wrap herself in a trance, leaving him outside to beat himself silly on the glass wall of her silence.

CHAPTER THREE

THE GLASS wall began to fail Alice, but Richard found his strength did not, as he had hoped, swell as hers ebbed. He was struggling to stay awake: in the dimness of the cell, the light of the grilled window dazzled his eyes and shut his lids. He stood up to call the gaoler. I'll have her run, he thought, and the truth will tumble out of her.

'Bridget,' she said suddenly.

'Bridget?' he pursued. 'Bridget, whose death you brought about? Your foster-daughter, who you betrayed?'

'No.' She said impatiently, 'No, not that, you fool. I shouldn't have told her so many ghost stories.'

He could get no more out of her.

ROBERT

I HAVE tampered with the records once. I have no strength to do it any more. What would be the sense in it? And everyone knows, even our Vicar, though he pretends to ignore it, that I, churchwarden of the parish of Whitchurch St Leonard, once authorised the payment of church money to a cunning woman who was later hanged as a witch. We have written the hanging into the book. Can I deny that I married her niece, who called her Mother?

It seemed a simple transaction at the time: Alice found

the Communion cup, and we paid her. It was not simple. Alice was the Devil's henchwoman, for one. And she had bait for me in her house, which I snapped up. Bridget. Must I always be the butt of pity, if not contempt?

At least Big Margaret's flight has saved me from poverty, though Alice destroyed so much of my livestock. I can lay claim to her mother's land now, and I will get it. But the claim will take time and effort, and Alice's land, these last years, has lain as fallow as they said it did in Francis's hands, before he married her. There is nothing for me but labour – and grief.

Yet if anyone had told me there's a sort of peace comes when everything's over, I'd never have believed them. The first time I was widowed, I was wild with joy. I could marry Bridget! This time I sit by the fire at night, and feel the heaviness of my body: I have always been a solid man, in my person as in office and worth. Now I am played out, and my hair is ashed with grey. In spite of which something inside me says it is time for a new beginning. I cannot bring my wife and children back again.

Margaret has buried Alice with Bridget and my boys in the churchyard. No one wanted to stop her. Not even I.

I used all my strength to detach Bridget, to open her eyes about Alice, who she would call Mother. I said, Francis Slade was always so haggard, died raving, didn't Alice ride him to hell every night?

I had bad dreams myself, my heart galloping, my body sweating – I would wake and put my fingers between my teeth, then thank God it was flesh I felt, not the cold iron bit. If ever I'd felt for Bridget and found her gone, I mightn't have been surprised. Or if I'd woken on the road, the two of us tumbling in the ditch because my hoofed front legs had turned back into arms. But Bridget wasn't Alice: she didn't have the wicked tongue. There's not a soul in this village – except me – who didn't loiter by Alice's garden from time to time to hear the tales she was telling her bees. You'd have thought she could creep through cracks, the things she talked about, right down to the winestain on John Tegg's pizzle. She must have changed herself into an eavesdropping, spying mouse.

She played to her audience, she'd cast a quick glance round and bring out some piece of scandal you really wanted to hear. Or so they say. I have no reason to doubt it. And so everyone in the village bribed her with food, firewood, yeast for beer, butter. And bought her honey from her. She lived well: she didn't need to work.

She knew too much.

And I'd find her in this house, wheedling, feeding cakes to the children – which were made of pickings from my larder – and holding the baby in her filthy hands. She was no fit grandmother for them. She was not their grand-mother, only they were made to give her the name. She gave my lads apples, cajoling them and smiling her false smile – it made me shiver to listen to her. Bridget knew what ruin witches can wreak if you let them feed an apple to a child. And she wouldn't forbid Alice the house! My wife was like a silly child when Alice was about, she let the foul creature poke her magic in under the bedstraw, rummage for this and that piece of food. 'Oh,' says she, 'Bridget' – a sidelong squint at me – 'you won't miss this, will you?'

It was intolerable. Whose house did my wife think she was living in?

And then poor Madam Berkeley died a miserable death, and her baby after her, and everyone knew – because Alice had told her bees – how her dog had pissed on the Reverend Berkeley's leg when he went to reason with Alice about her godless behaviour. It was the day of the funeral she came into my house again, and put her hands out for the babe.

'I will not have this,' I said. 'You are not to touch my children.'

Her face sharpened with malice, her faded green eyes narrowed and darkened between their uneven lids, and her lank cheeks flushed: I need only close my eyes to see it. And hear her words, directed at Bridget:

'You only prosper with my permission.' I shall never forget. Nor the sight of the children, the next day, jaws locked, their eyes turning upwards and froth coming out of their mouths, ruin all around us, betrayed by my wife. I cannot think otherwise.

Because I told Bridget that strong faith and prayer would armour her against Alice. Did she believe me? She sat shivering and whimpering, and her fear spread to the children. When they lay dying, and she fetched the piece of thatch from Alice's roof, when she set fire to it on our hearth, she did it only to confirm her despair.

She had to give evidence, to loosen the bond. And she knew so much more than I did, she could tell the court everything she had seen over the years, and what Alice had tried to make of her. I promised her the freedom she'd always craved, when Alice was burned – we all thought Alice would burn. Even the judge, till the clerk told him otherwise. Everyone knows the evil dies with the witch whose body is burned up. If not, it passes to her children. The law has put Margaret in peril now, and God knows how many more. It is hard to believe all they would do for us was hang her. Though however she died, it came too late for Bridget.

What did she tell her bees about me? Who was listening? No, there is no peace, after all. Does the village know all about its churchwarden, or did her death come in time for me?

You hear the small noises in a house, when you're alone in it. And I hear rustlings from the past: the bed shakes under my first wife Lisbeth and all the men she entertained in it while I was working. I can hear her squeaks of pleasure, soft as a mouse. And the tiptoe footsteps of the dairymaid, who was paid to keep her mouth shut. I can hear my own heavy tread one day – my breath sucked in as I looked at the two of them lying in wanton and naked sleep – and hear my retreating steps. The house will tell me that story over, again and again now I'm alone.

Cold tonight: you can see the frost on the inside of the walls, and white ferns spread over the windows. The days get longer and the cold gets stronger. Always the doubt about the spring: will it come now? Will the wheat grow again, or will it crook down yellow and lie dead on the earth?

Time to geld the lambs. Work goes on, which is a mercy. And there's plenty to do for a man on his own. Though the maid knows her job. Bridget trained her well.

The rushlight is flickering in the draughts: the shadows run forward, retreat, mouth at me like ghosts. Hungry ghosts. How is it for Bridget and Alice, out there in the cold flinty earth with the children? Do they writhe together like a knot of earthworms? Here I sit on my own, jumping like an idiot at shadows.

Bridget.

She's everywhere, all of a sudden. I can hear her voice, see her face, feel her body in my arms. And desire her as desperately as I did before we were married. 'Oh, Robert,' she said, 'save me, take me away from Mother, she'll kill me,' she said, 'she'll eat me alive.'

Hadn't I learned my lesson, after Lisbeth? I was a fool to take Bridget out of that family. Her father unknown – that was the kindest thing you could say. If the rumours were true she was a thing so unnatural she should have been throttled at birth. But I shut my ears to any bad talk about her.

I thought I could save her: I prayed about it, fervent professor of the faith that I was then – well, fervour fades. And the light of God on your actions dims and goes out. Instead you hear Lust, and Theft, spoken in the voice of judgement. What do I learn from that? Do I learn that I'm damned?

My dead wife's shadow stands by the wall, listening to my thoughts, agreeing with everything I say, though it makes her snivel and wipe her nose on the back of her hand. She's another whore, must I always wed with whores? Only she's given her body to death, not lovers, for the pleasure of dissolution. But tonight her flesh is still entire, her face not as smooth as it was, but childishly round. Her figure, though, that's not childish. She smiles, through her tears, at this commendation. Oh, so meek, I chose you because you were meek. I didn't guess the secrets. You were sly, my Bridget. Tell me, what did you really want of me, or don't you know, even now? And what can a dead body know, rotting in its coffin, waiting to rise again on the last day?

Or not.

The fire falls apart in a shower of bright sparks. I jump. The rushlight has burned low, and I can't see another: the shadows are a multitude all at once, waiting their opportunity to dart, smother, strangle. Quick, more wood. My chilled hands are clumsy. So much labour, so much fear. And the wood is damp. It doesn't want to burn. The rushlight. I must find another rushlight. Here. I am safe. Now I can see the fire.

I should never have gone to the war: Bridget was too weak a woman to leave. And the war unleashed strong powers of evil – didn't it, Bridget? You know all about it. Oh yes.

But are you really Bridget, are you my wife, where are the children, how could you leave them alone in the earth? Are you a devil come to make a witch of me? It's against the law to entertain wicked spirits. Have I been speaking aloud? Did the maid hear me?

Go to the door. Yes, that's right. Go, without me. Where would you lead me, fiend? Beckon to me all you like, make Bridget's half-guilty smile. You won't entice me out into the dark.

RICHARD said: 'You thought you were in special favour with Satan, did you not? You could amuse yourself with all of us as you did with that poor drunken fool Simon.'

Returned to her chains, she panted and shook, her tongue flopping in her mouth. She felt piss run warm down her leg: there, she thought, is some more stink for Richard Berkeley's curling nostrils.

He said: 'He has deceived others in this way. I have books. I have read it all. The Witchcraft Act, under which you are condemned, proves it. Malefice is a treacherous gift Satan uses to entrap silly old women.' Pulling his foot away to avoid the runnel of yellow, straw-stuck liquid, he challenged her: 'You didn't want the children killed. Did he care about that?'

I couldn't fly away, she thought, the walls are too solid.

'We proved the truth,' he said. 'The bees came to seek you out. Did you hear Satan laughing when he had you in the trap?'

Her legs were still running against her will, hustled by the two men whose bodies she could still feel, close either side of her, slapping her when she tried to let herself drop.

'They came, yes,' she said. 'Poor innocent tiny fools.'

'Didn't your bees help you hurt your neighbours, woman?'

'I did right to hurt them. I knew I had the power. They wouldn't help an old woman. Sarah Tidbury tried to steal my bees.'

'You had no power, Alice. Satan cheated you. Satan destroyed the children, to torment you. He is not your friend.'

'No one is my friend.'

'I am your friend, Alice.'

'Liar,' she said, spat, and laughed.

SARAH

MY LIVING half can't drag my dead half around, so I keep to my bed. I'm a useless old wreck of a woman. And the dead eye cheats the other, so neither sees anything but fog. I mess the sheets. Audrey gets angry with me, but when she can't wait for me to finish with the nightpot, can't hurry to me when I need it, who's to blame, tell me that? Then she says she doesn't understand what I'm saying. Undutiful slug of a daughter-in-law my son's saddled me with, and so ill-favoured – doesn't it look badly on me, that my son chose a plain woman?

Once I'd wind my hair round the wheat-stalks at harvest. The colour was the same. I was a straight woman, I had lovely breasts, blue-grey eyes and a white skin, even in summer. I was the one the boys loved. I was such a pretty dancer! And even the gentry took notice. Sir Henry Berkeley – our parson's elder brother, who went to France with the Prince – he called me by a Greek name, wrote a poem about me, and read it to his friends. I was a handsome old woman. What have I done to deserve this?

I only took a swarm of bees out of my pear tree. Alice said they were hers, but she had no proof. So I wouldn't give them back to her. She sent her dog to piss on my cottage wall, the next day I was like this. Now I'm a burden on Martin and Audrey. After so many years of dreading her revenge, I grew careless.

I lie here thinking, hearing the pig grunt outside. Waiting for death, piggy and I. Which will go first?

They said her death would kill the bad magic, but it did me no good. I couldn't get to the trial, and I never saw the hanging. I'm uglier than Alice ever was. They remember my good looks to gloat about their passing.

Against the fog Alice has made for me, I see her face twice over: the bitter old face, one eyelid drooping, brown age-spots, folds like carved wood, the brittle-sharp chin, tufts of orangy-white hair about the cheeks – you've aged badly, Alice, everyone hates you. Then here's the skinny young new-moon face with the green slant eyes under the red hair, the face that could sour or sweeten in an instant – and sometimes you'd almost have said she was beautiful.

I have to remember her hands, white as birch, for all they were forever working, smooth, and warm on you when she touched you. And now I see my own lost comely face, sometimes watching Alice, sometimes refusing to see her. Masks, all of them.

Alice Slade, our cunning woman, and later our witch. Bridget's aunt (and her murderer), mother to Big Margaret with her meek carriage and her salt tongue, daughter to the cunning man Ralfe Gibbons, and his wife the midwife Lydia, sister to Juliet who died in disgraceful childbirth, and to Jacob, the idiot who drowned in the mill-pond. Francis Slade's wife – to his torment – slut to our one-time parson, the Ranter Sykes, and to a tawdry pretty tumbler whose name I never knew.

She was there all my life. Now she's gone. Gone to hell, I hope. But Parson says I might find her in heaven because she confessed. He says I shouldn't want to see her burn. He asked me was I so sure of heaven? Oh, but haven't I been chaste, haven't I denied myself?

I want to fish her out of the flames, feel her gratitude, feel her kiss me. Then throw her back, because she ran away with the tumbler. There's a hole in this sheet. The disgrace of it, my son's a well-off farmer, and his wife palms me off with holes in the sheets! The tumbler never looked at me. He looked at her.

I was a wife and I kept my reputation clean. I had three sons, the two best of them stolen from me by the Parliament, and wasted in the war. Fighting for their rights, that's what they said they were doing. Their right to lie in six feet of earth?

Alice sat astride the mountebank's upright cock, his hands on her little breasts, hers all over his chest, his shoulders, his thighs, searching, caressing, exciting him – I hate her for it, how dared she, how could she? None of the rest of us could have run off for a year of pleasure.

Alice used her hands on her clients, when they were sick, on me when I bore Martin and everyone else in the house was laid flat with the fever. I can hear her voice now, coaxing me, honey-sweet, calling me her love.

I knew the swarm was hers, I took her fat brown bees because I wanted to take the honey away from her. I wanted to leave her with nothing but dry bread. But she was the stronger. I thought I'd starve her into speaking to me again, she didn't speak to me, not even to complain or curse, she spoke to my son to demand her bees back. She knew how to keep her mouth shut.

The bees all flew out of the hive Martin put them in, and made their way straight to her in prison. That proved they were her evil spirits. I should have destroyed them while they clustered and hung on my tree.

They say it was a good hanging.

★

RICHARD said: 'You must understand this, Alice. I am trying to save you from everlasting torment.' He fingered his parson's bands and watched her vicious old face.

She said: 'You're starving me because your son starved. I'm glad he died. You're tormenting me because you tormented your wife – and I did right when I made her die. She always pretended she was too good for this world. You needed the harm, all of you, so I hurt you. You were ready for it. Now you hate me.' She saw his Adam's apple jump in his neck.

My sin, he thought, opens a channel for Satan. My weakness, bringing contagion to all about me. Why can't I believe in Susan now, at least when she is dead? The doubts gnaw at me and shred me, I shiver and cry for pain – and this foul hag sees it.

She turned her head towards the dazzle of the cell window. She said: 'Only the fairies were my friends. In their own way. They have no feelings left, their hearts withered a long time ago. But they stopped coming to me. Maybe *she* died, you know – no, you don't know. And anyway, she withered like the rest of them, and left me alone for ever.' She began to shake. 'I'm cold,' she said. 'I'm tired. I'm hungry. Hold me. I'm lonely.'

Reluctantly, he put a hand on her shoulder. She laid her head on it – his stomach heaved with qualms of unwelcome pity. Her dirty hair irritated his skin – it was too much contact.

He asked: 'Who was *she*?'

'The one they took away and left me behind. I tried to live like a human, but I don't know what to do, the way the rest of you seem to. And when I asked her how, she'd forgotten.'

He thought: If she asked me how, would I be able to tell her? He bit his lips on the confession.

Alice's knees groaned with strain. She thought: Warm savoury food in my belly. Then sleep.

SARAH

MY OLD body pinned down the way it is, my mind goes staggering round it. I knew Alice longer than anyone: surely I should understand? How she could destroy Bridget, who she suckled with the milk her own dead child didn't need. How she could take pleasure in tormenting us all, when once she was pleased to help us, found our property, told our fortunes, dosed our sickness away and set our bones. And mended black witchcraft. Did that entrap her?

What did she say all those years ago, when we looked in the silver bowl together? I saw what I wanted, saw myself in Martin Tidbury's arms. I was so pleased that I asked her what she saw, even teased her that there might be a lover there for her, though I didn't believe it. If she saw the tumbler that day, she kept him quiet.

She looked for a long time, seemed to flinch once or twice, pressed her lips together. Then such a longing came into her face: I thought, That's it, she has seen a lover. Even Alice. I thought, well, if they didn't look at her face and skimpy body, if they shut their eyes and felt her hands on them, they might well think it worthwhile to banish the light.

And she said: 'Darkness.' Her voice was soft and deep, and her eyes went to slits in her face. Something wriggled sweetly, deep in my belly. The cobwebs in her father's house shook as if a door had been opened, but the door was tight shut. She said: 'Foxglove, velvet darkness. I want it, Sarah.'

I thought: She's beautiful, after all. The thought scared me. Then I thought: It's the rushlight. There's so much you can't see by rushlight. I thought: She's not lovelier than I am. I'm the one who's beautiful. I always will be.

I didn't know what to answer, but I said: 'What we want is mostly what we can't have.' I laughed nervously. I knew I was talking out of place.

She glanced at me as if she'd rather I wasn't there. That hurt.

She said: 'Sixpennyworth of knowledge, that's what you want, all of you.'

It was worse because what she was saying tugged at me, as if I *ought* to know, as if – as she seemed to think – I was a fool to have mislaid the knowledge. I got angry.

I asked: 'You think you're different? You Gibbonses have fairy blood, so you can have what you want while the rest of us go without? And maybe your blood is stranger even than your father's and your little sister's?' Now swallow that, I thought.

She spat at me – our friendship was always pitted with quarrels.

She said: 'You want to know where you dropped your best knife, or the silver piece with its edges clipped ragged. What I see in here, not all the petty belongings in the world would pay for it. You want to find who laid an enchantment on you, but if you could see what I see, no one would ever be able to touch you again. And you want a lover' – I felt as if a snake was looking me over – 'but this pleasure is worlds better. Oh, it's a crime to tell you. You'll never understand.'

She was jealous. I can see that. So she wanted to make nothing of me. I'm glad I never understood her. Her knowledge was the kind that burns you to black screaming cinders in hell.

A snake, that's my memory of her that day. Maybe I really saw her other shape, maybe she slid among us, carrying poison. But I was blind, in those days. I was angry, and scared, but I wouldn't see the evil in her.

CHAPTER FOUR

SIR THOMAS

THE COMMON people can be controlled by such excitements, being in a more rudimentary stage of development. I am convinced I was right to allow Alice Slade's case to go forward to the Assizes. Witchcraft – maybe, maybe not. But we live on the brink of anarchy: the danger is greater now than ever before. And we who took Parliament's side must recognise our own blame. We made the New Model Army to overthrow the King, and it became a breeding ground for disorder.

Liberty has a sharp and double edge, only fit to be handled by just and virtuous men. I am Justice of the Peace: I have my responsibility.

It feels safe, in here. The carved panelling is warmed by the flames from the log fire; my eyes, drowsing, see my new Dutch tulips' red and yellow parrot heads flowering against the black furred chimney – but the tulips are outside, their new shoots shivering in the wind.

Unreason comes rushing in from the dark and breaks on the walls like seawater: it takes labour and forethought to keep the defences up. I fear those oak panels may yet crack and break apart, and ravening werewolves burst into the room. God – though he does not exist – must keep the mob in check. And Hell, and a Devil to make them tremble. And a king, too, if necessary. I recognised that on the day Charles Stuart was executed. But a king we can mould.

There was that fellow I saw running through the streets of London, babbling about wealth and privilege. They can print what they like these days, the lettered fools fuddle the unlettered with half-chewed poison. We suffer the consequences. Yet there must be hope. In spite of the miasma of religious enthusiasm, the nightmare of dispossession. It might even be that we have come to a crossroads. If only we can strengthen what has proved its worth in the past, while turning away from sectarian lunacy!

And from Eve, so old and savage, all filthy with blood and earth. Or her descendant, my wife Marjorie, who is all too lustily alive. While Richard Berkeley's Susan is dead, who was gentle and docile as my spaniel bitches. I should have been given Susan, and Richard Berkeley deserves Marjorie to wife – she'd whip his tail between his legs.

One day we will banish the dark. We will build a world of men, clean, strong, fit for men to live in. So says my head, but my belly turns, since I must go now to my bed, and there my wife's carnal gate yawns wide, waiting to engulf me.

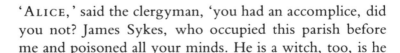

'ALICE,' said the clergyman, 'you had an accomplice, did you not? James Sykes, who occupied this parish before me and poisoned all your minds. He is a witch, too, is he not?'

He watched her face, willing her to open her mouth and speak the words his mind was thinking for her. Her lips parted – It is happening, he thought – but they spread wide to show her teeth, and her face made a silent grimace of malice, need, and repellent grief. He shrank back into his chair: It is myself I see there, he thought, she is showing me my naked loathsome soul.

JAMES SYKES

IT IS a wonder, even now in the midst of my grief, how life turns the world upside down. Once I was the angry young Puritan parson of Whitchurch St Leonard. Thinking the world was within a few years or even months of its ending, I was convinced that Alice, with her divinations and her potions, was no better than the Witch of Endor, maybe even the very Whore of Babylon on her scarlet-coloured beast, against whom the writer of Revelation bears witness. My bile was shared between Alice and Henrietta Maria Stuart, by attacking both of whom I thought to save my soul. For my pamphlet against the Papist Queen they whipped me through the streets and cut off my ears. I do not regret this mutilation. Once the lying voices of this world were numbed, I could hear the voice of God within me. Then my search for truth began.

Men call me a Ranter, but I say of myself, a Seeker. I have tried all the Sects who propose a better way, Levellers, Diggers, Anabaptists, Quakers – the last nearest to my condition. Yet none of them satisfies me. Let them call me what they like. I am on my path.

They closed their ears when I spoke out against Alice. Now they have done what I wanted all those years ago. I am alone again, in opposition to them again, the only one to understand that she was really good. I shall be cold every night that I cannot return to her.

I shall be cold.

I thought she was a fox asleep, the day I found her at her parents' grave, the morning of the storm, when the old yew crashed down on top of the church gateway. I went to look, she opened her eyes, and I saw an innocent hurt child. Oh yes, I know they say I'm crazy. Maybe you have to be crazy to see such things.

SIR THOMAS

RICHARD BERKELEY of all men to preach virtue to her! The King's man, always ready to swear allegiance to whoever was in power: Archbishop Laud's man who turned Presbyterian and preached a sermon to celebrate his leader's execution. Ridicule, contempt – he deserves them all. He never deserved Susan's love.

Nor did he get rid of the chalice and altar-cloth he'd forced on the village when ceremony was the fashion for the Church: he took them to Lord Smale to hide – another timeserver. He went back and preached a sermon against idolatries. If the congregation hadn't been nine-tenths asleep, they'd have laughed him out of his pulpit. Then they turned out in the afternoon to hear the crop-eared Sykes, because they'd always liked him. Sykes may spread as much sedition as he pleases now – we *must* bring back laws that once muzzled him and his ilk. And since he can hardly hear anything, his brain is able to ferment uninterrupted. They turn out to hear his sort as they might to watch bear-baiting and travelling players, against whom there is a law. Yet which is more dangerous?

There might, I suppose, be danger in Richard Berkeley – beyond the danger he posed to anyone who tried to weave their happiness with his. Does he act according to strategy? Water moulds itself to every obstacle, yet rubs them all away in time. I will prove it, when the new King returns. But has Richard the wit to work in this way?

If he has, then he is a threat, since he has plenty of grievances to set him against me. He is the second son of the house I now inhabit – and will pass on to my own son. I bought it from the Commonwealth, who took it from his brother. He makes it clear that he thinks me a jumped-up clown – and no doubt blames me for his family's departure.

However shabby a life Sir Henry Berkeley must lead in France, I'll wager he's glad to escape his brother's company. So mournful, Richard Berkeley, our shepherd of souls. Yet clever enough to keep his place when better men have been thrust out of theirs. Or desperate enough.

But my worst crime was my feeling for Susan. He wanted to eat away at her peace of mind without observation or reproach from his peers. He says he hated his years in the wilds of Cumberland – but there only sheep could bleat in at the windows to see what he was doing to his wife.

Oh, I am safe on all counts. He has no wit. Or else he'd have got the witch to implicate Sykes. His trouble is, he has faith. Credulous fool.

IT HURT her, to remain silent. I will have to speak, she thought, but it must be later rather than sooner.

SIMON

SLIPPING about. Trouble with drinking, the roads get as wet as your belly does. Sing a song, singing, you don't feel lonely.

> For still would he cry, a Ratt tat tat
> Tara, Rat, ever.

We won the war. Poor bastard won the war. New heaven, new earth, rights, that's what we fought for, man's right to get drunk? Only there still isn't enough money to do it every night of the week. Poor Simon Sharpe, sober as hell, three days out of the seven.

Dark. Nobody can look at me now. Dark as hell. No,

hell's not dark, all lit up with flames. In the Army, you heard people talking, Ranters, Diggers, said there was no such thing as hell.

Arguments, tearing you like the crows on the field at Naseby. Ideas.

We won. They won. Like Sarah Tidbury's lads with their horses and fine equipment, and 'Come with me, lad, you're for the Army.'

New heaven, new earth. Still as many rats. Kill them with my teeth. War hero. They buy me drinks to pretend they can stand the sight of my face. Even that's wearing off. King or Cromwell, I can't get drunk seven nights a week. Never got paid.

Lucky it was my left arm I lost. I can put down poison for vermin. Rats, mice, moles. And pull out a few recipes for the French pox. Oh, I know a thing or two. The mercuries, and cantharies, and arsenic, and roseacre.

Moles, nice black creatures, burrowing about in the darkness – what's the point of saving the farmer's crops? I'll still be sober three days out of the seven.

> He was so brave a bowser
> That it was doubtful whether
> He taught the rats, or the rats taught him
> To be drunk as rats, together.

Fool song, rats aren't drunk, try the bait, walk away, if they feel ill they don't come back. Sober as hell. Sober as judges.

The rat sat up there in his robes, sent the witch to the gallows. So much shouting she couldn't hear us accuse her. She knew. No need for her to hear.

All the half-hour she jerked on the rope, the sun shone bright and you couldn't see her shadow. There wasn't one. I sold a lot of medicine there. I belong there, fit in somehow.

Everyone staring at her. It took such a long time to die.

'The Army might make a man of you,' said my mother, and tossed back another pot of ale. It spilled all down her. If she'd been alive to see what the Army made of me, the shock might have sobered her up for an hour or so. You can still smell the ale-fumes round her grave.

It's safe to be out in the dark now. I shan't see that Thing again, I was sober enough to slit its throat. With its red eyes and its mane like a horse, as big as a horse. Huffing at my back. Huff and huff and huff and huff.

Thieving old whore, I called her. She made a bastard of me.

Grave men listening, writing it down – what they could hear of it. Hustled me out when I asked for money, fought for Commonwealth. Poor man. It takes such a long time to die.

Huff and huff and huff and huff.

Fear, behind you, daren't turn to look. Don't like darkness now.

Witch never really repented, or she'd have cast a shadow, confession was a fake, black dog didn't really die, coming up behind me, red collar of blood round its neck, eyes as red as hell, teeth hungry for me. Behind me.

Huff and huff and huff and huff.

I can't run any more. Can't look round. Got to keep going. Light burning in the alehouse.

My feet, stuck in the mud.

JANE

SIR THOMAS, up there in's big house, feeds me till I give my evidence. Then he throws me out: 'I'll starve in the ditch,' say I, 'widowed, and no one to support the babe

and me.' And fieldwork paid at a penny a day for women.
'That's your affair,' says he, 'as long as you're out of this
parish, and we don't have the expense of your burial.
Take your shiftless self off,' says he, 'did you think you
could live on me for ever? You ought to be grateful to
me,' says Sir Thomas, 'for having employed a married
man, and having let you live in the parish you don't
belong to.' So I went to his wife, and she gave me a few
shillings: better than nothing. He's frightened of her, so
he beds with the serving maids. When they come out with
a great belly, it's my lady who has to deal with them. And
what was going on between him and the Vicar's poor
wife? People talk.

He stands tall, looking down on me, but he was a
grocer, was Lord Mayor, Cromwell's knight – and sends
letters to the Royalists in France. Handsome and grave as
any lord, he must have thought he was wasted, behind a
counter.

'The witch killed your husband,' says he. My man
would be alive still, if Sir Thomas hadn't been too stingy
to spare a few pence for honey. But you can't touch *his*
conscience. He asks: 'Aren't you glad we brought her to
justice?' Well, while the hunt was up, I was glad to join
in, while I still had food in my belly.

CHAPTER FIVE

JUDITH

But what I should have done was, I should have put the red hot poker in the cream, that day I knew the witch was spoiling the butter. T'other wisewoman told me. 'If you're here,' I should have said, 'have at your eye.' I might have blinded her. The poker worked when her grandson shat at my door, after the trial. I heard him yell when I thrust it in his droppings. He felt it in his arse all right. But Margaret has taken all that bad blood away to plague some other neighbourhood.

I'm a tall strong woman, well respected round here. I do my hair neatly, my caps are always clean and crisp. I make our clothes well, every thread evenly woven, every stitch neat and small. I get a good price for my wool. Why didn't I counter bad magic with good, instead of seeking Alice out with empty scolding, giving her room to curse me again?

Who'll ever forget it was my daughter whose hands were turned back to front? I'm disgraced. Can I forget how she screamed, and I screamed along with her? And then I heard Alice's laughter. She was nowhere near, John saw her the other end of the village, picking dropwort. My husband doesn't lie.

To think once we went to Alice for help against black witchcraft. And a few other things. She soured, they say now. I say she was always playing a double game, and I know I'm right. You can't really trust cunning folk. They

39

know too much. If I'd spoken about what I saw, years ago, in her house, they might have believed me. Maybe not then. Now I'm believed.

Butter's good to work with today, winter's the best time, not like summer, when it just runs through your fingers. I like a job well done. Washed, squeezed, and moulded, a flower-shape atop each one, the pats lie ready for a sale, and for use. I make good money for our house. Winter or summer. All but the time Alice spoiled my butter for me, spoiled everything for herself, only for the sake of a piece of yeast.

You have to look out for yourself these days, and have an eye to spare for the maid idling. Times are hard. I dealt with Alice myself, after all. If more of us had acted promptly – but most of them are thriftless, weak-willed folk, so frightened of causing offence, they let Alice scare them and cajole them. They'd never have swum her if John and I hadn't cornered the old hag in her cottage.

I like a job well done. I did everything the wisewoman told me. I did it properly. Only my little Anne didn't want to scratch Alice, she wouldn't do anything with her hands the way they were. She looked down at her useless splayed palms and whimpered for fear. I had to take hold of them and scrab Alice's cheek hard with the nails, so the blood came. Anne and Alice screamed at the same moment, as if they were one person, for God's sake!

Alice stopped fighting John – she'd struggled so hard, she'd thrown her chair down – and went limp all at once, beaten, you might say. Biding her time, more like. The Devil himself was looking out of her eyes. And my knees were shaking, but no one could see that under my skirt.

But once Anne's hands were right again, she fell on Alice, scratching at her face. I sobbed for relief and joy while our witness, Will Corfe, threw the door open, ran out, and shouted up and down the street: 'Come and swim the witch!'

Suddenly we were all laughing as we dragged her to the pond; only Bridget didn't come, she and Robert sat in the house and let us do the work for them. Did Bridget still think Alice was her mother, did she care more for that hag than for her dead children?

The water wouldn't have her: it pushed her to the surface, so we knew we could take her to court. Someone got hold of the black cur and threw that in: it proved to be the devil's creature too. Alice howled when its throat was slit. Like a dog. I know what I make of that. But never a tear came out. You can tell a witch by her tearlessness, and I hold to this: I never saw Alice weep. Anyone who says they did is a liar.

I had to act. Why should she have been allowed to go on whining from door to door, frightening us all out of a piece of yeast here, a cup of flour there? It was an offence to all of us, even if worse hadn't happened.

How could she? I would never shame myself like that. I am a God-fearing, hard-working woman. I've seen the weak and shiftless go down. Fear is a good spur to enterprise. Alice used to be proud: she never asked a favour of anyone. Then, all of a sudden, she couldn't do a good job of work anywhere. She let her bowl tarnish black as soot and gabbled some nonsense at her clients that did nobody any good. She and old Sykes, ranting together. Her cow strayed and never came back, her sheep grew maggotty and rotted away – she knew how to treat them, and she didn't. Her vegetables shot into flower and seed and the weeds ran everywhere over her ground. She had no more wool to sell in town, but now and again you'd see her spinning idly from a filthy clump of fleece, making great knots in the wool and forever breaking off.

What got into her brains and destroyed them? A woman

never needs even to wonder what comes next, her occupations slide through her fingers, shaped by her hand, always running, running, the family's needs are the fleece we spin from – Alice, all of a sudden, answered the question none of us ever ask, and her answer was: Nothing. Nothing comes next. So she went bad.

It's the times we've been through that are so unsettling. And all through the war, desperate people flocked to Alice for charms. Maybe they wore her out? The war changed everything. The village split like a pea-pod, tenants fell out on their landlords' side, and the freeholders, who had nothing to lose, on the side of Parliament, who seemed to promise small folk more. A few wise souls stayed in the pod and waited for the outcome. Like John. But most of the men began to brawl about politics, drunk or sober, and an instant later, or so it seemed, the hottest heads were off to the war.

From which many of them never came back, though our clever churchwarden did. Bridget's man. Lisbeth's before that. I was a child, but I knew what was going on there. How he shut his eyes to his wife's lovers, how he demanded nothing of her, pretending to believe in the illness she lied to him about, while all the time her legs were open to all comers. Did he hope he'd keep her, if he let her be, did he love her so much, or was he only afraid of ridicule? He got the ridicule. Lisbeth ran off with a twenty-year-old farmhand and died of drink and the young man's beatings. When Robert heard of it he thought he was in favour with God. So he took another wife. And never spoke Lisbeth's name again. He likes secrets, does Robert Tarry, he goes quaking for fear we might find out what we've known for years.

Oh, he's never been the same since he came back. The cannonball frightened him too badly when it brushed him on the battlefield. It was after that he began to bully

Bridget. And he saw Harry Tidbury smashed to a pulp. Sarah's child.

You have to feel sorry for old Sarah, she set so much store by looks and that lad was just like her, handsome, fair, every girl in the village had time for him. And Harry was modest with it, though that wasn't Sarah's doing. With Matthew already dead, poor Sarah, when the news came about Harry they thought she'd gone mad. She walked round the village for days, washing her hands, washing her face in any water that was nearby: she'd rub her wet hands over her face and look bewildered, as if she'd hoped to wash the truth away. And then her husband died, old Martin, and that, which ought to have driven her over the edge, brought her back to herself. She grieved, but no worse than any other widow. She'd accepted the world, as we all have to. But praise God my husband cared too much about his family to hare off after a cause and leave his body on a battlefield.

The war scarred the gentry, too. Lord Smale mourns his two sons, who went to opposite sides and met in our village street to fight out their childhood enmities for good and all; they lay dead on the frozen mud, while two of our women bled their lives out inside their houses, and half a dozen troopers joined the pilgrimage to the other world. The King's men, who won, took most of our animal fodder and stored food away with them. We went hungry, that winter.

And our Vicar, Richard Berkeley, who didn't want to follow his brother to penury in France, the war made him suffer. Leaving aside whatever it cost his conscience to grind his principles in the mud. Dangerous times, especially to men's consciences, though we've never heard so many lofty ideas.

Parson Berkeley, who started off with enough lofty ideas for twenty, neglected what was closest to hand – his own wife. Poor Madam Berkeley, she was a sweet pretty woman, and too kindly. If she'd been less kindly, he might have believed her when she told him she loved him. Which he could never believe: 'You despise me,' says he to her, I've heard him at it. And when Sir Thomas took over Sir Henry Berkeley's estates, handsome Sir Thomas with his face far nobler than Richard Berkeley's though his birth is low, and a straight back and fine head of hair and a smile for Madam Berkeley, who he favoured for being meeker far than his own wife – there was the mischief all ready to brew. Who knows what was between the two of them? Maybe Alice knew, but I was at the Vicarage one day about a recipe Madam Berkeley wanted from me, and I saw Sir Thomas kiss her in the garden.

She liked Sir Thomas. And since the Vicar told his wife ten times a day that she despised him, he may have convinced her in the end. So he must have been satisfied. Maybe he wanted us to despise him. We did.

There was a time when our Vicar prayed for the King's victory on Sundays, a time when he prayed for nothing more than an end to the conflict, and a time when he prayed for Parliament. So then we knew who was going to win the war. We already knew the colour of our Vicar's liver. But we let be. Those who cared about ideas were away fighting for them, and none of the men who stayed behind wanted to cause trouble.

I've changed. I've grown sharper, tougher. John and I have our brats to look after. I've learned. Some of Lord Smale's tenants thought they were clever: the moment the Vicar prayed for Parliament in Church, they stopped paying their rents – but he didn't lose his estates as they thought, he was fined, and he has to get the money back from somewhere. He found himself new tenants who would pay, and higher rents at that. Sir Thomas needs money, too: Sir Henry's sequestrated land didn't come cheap, so he's pushed the rents up, and evicted the unreliable payers. And if he can enclose a field rather than keep a shepherd, that's what he does, to save paying out wages. No victories for the poor. Thank God we're freeholders.

Now some of them get their heads together and complain the times are bleak – no ballad-singing, they moan, no players, no sports. A bare church and a long sermon. At least it keeps your mind on your work. And there are opportunities, if you're prepared to put your back into it: God rewards the diligent. I'm a practical woman. I take the world as I find it.

JAMES SYKES

THIS WORLD, in which the gross see only grossness, is lit from within by a God forever present, never by the dim lantern-light coming out of the windows of churches – barren steeple-houses, gaol-houses locked up by hireling priests. No, the light is in green trees and bright flowers, the dark earth, the sun and the moon, the silver fish and the furred beasts, and the birds that used to fly to Alice when she chirruped to them. In ourselves, could we but take down the shutters of self-deception.

There is no sin. Everything comes by nature, and nature is good. Sin is a word they have made out of their own fears. They fear life, as I did.

I wrapped myself up in black, throttled myself with a pair of white bands, held a heavy book ready to fend off attacks on what I deemed my purity. I strayed among the black letters of deceiving books, and learned hatred, subservience, and evil. Their vaunted chastity is nothing but the deepest, most disgusting vice. Dung on a heap –

being of nature – is cleaner far than the miasmic vapours of so-called Christian marriage. We must be free of all such unnatural bonds. How dare the husband say the wife is his property?

But that cold night when I lay beside Alice at last, when we turned to each other, naked flesh to naked flesh, and knew each other fully – we were with God, then. Or are love and tenderness and gentle pleasure the creatures of the Devil? I will not believe it. We are called, in the end, to *be*. Nothing else matters.

The war was fought to abolish tyranny, but it left tyranny untouched, because the worst tyranny is within us. I have suffered pain and shame in my search for truth. I fought at Naseby, argued, though it was difficult because of my hearing, at Putney for a world truly renewed, thought always of this or that outward circumstance as the enemy – now false religion, now hireling priests, now corrupt Parliaments, now property. I was defeated, every time. These things will fall away of their own accord if we renew ourselves. We must cast off the wicked and lying moralities of the past. Must be free, in summer, to go unclad and feel the wind on our bodies – which wind is the true Holy Spirit, comforting us. So should we be a sign to all men that God is within us, and we need be ashamed of nothing.

Our old caressing fingers undid oppression: it slid off us like our clothes. Then at last we were free, Alice and I.

'Sykes, Alice, tell me what you did with Sykes?'

'What did you say? I can't hear.'

I frightened him, she thought, when he came to scold at my door. He had no gaoler behind him then, no chains, and when my dog baptised his leg for him, he thought he'd drop dead on the spot.

'I don't give a fart for your church,' I said, 'now you've no court to drag me to. Misery,' I said, 'that's what your church has given us, and a host of grasping divines who are never satisfied with what they can claw out of poor people's pockets.'

I laughed: he tried to halt away with dignity, but the piss had run into his boot and he squelched as he went.

'Alice,' he said now, his voice pleading where it should threaten, 'it is growing late. Night is coming, death will come in the morning.'

But he thought: It has already come. Susan's voice sounded in his ears: 'Why will you never trust me?' it asked. 'I love you. What does it matter about your leg, what does it matter what the rest of them think, don't I bear your babies for you – ?' He thought: No. I shall never ask the witch what she knows about my son's parentage. And that Susan didn't love me, that's sure. No one could love me.

Alice said: 'I'm not afraid of the dark.'

He shivered. He asked: 'How do you find your way through the dark with no light to guide you?'

She said: 'I don't need to find my way. It comes to me, as I wait.' The words grew out of the lightness of hunger: she wondered at them herself.

I'm getting lost, he thought, and a little boy cried in the empty room for a mother who had shut him in. The child's suffering rose and engulfed the limping adult man. He thought he saw a cane in Alice's hand, saw authority in her upright figure.

The witch is mad, he thought. No, she's possessed, and she's possessing me, too.

'No,' he said. 'No, I don't want to be in the dark.'

Alice thought: He's still afraid. So why am I in chains and why does he sit like a judge in a chair?

A drop of water splashed onto his head and bounced

off. He put his hand to his cold wet scalp and tried to dry it. He thought: I shan't come out of this with my wits about me. I should never have shut myself up with her.

Alice said: 'You talk about truth and falsehood as if they could be weighed out like dried peas. But you don't really want the truth, nobody does. We all want short weight, and have it made up with falsehood. Then we feel safe.'

His fingers were still worrying at his scalp when another drip fell on him.

'Why don't you move?' asked Alice. 'And haven't you got a handkerchief?'

He moved.

'You see?' said Alice. 'I care about you.' She croaked with laughter.

MARGARET

MY FOSTER-SISTER Bridget wanted people to frighten her; then she could bury her head in her hands and they'd comfort her. I was ready to do the frightening, but not the comforting. There were others to pity Bridget – my mother obliged. Though she did worse frightening on her own account, did my mother.

I knew Bridget well, because I loved her. You love your dinner, don't you? I wanted to eat her, I wanted to become her. I really believed one day I could manage it. When I lay in bed with Thomas, didn't I imagine I was her? Thomas perched on me like a child on a carthorse, and I began to shrink like wool in the wash. Now she's dead, I can't do it any more. I don't want to be a corpse. Thomas is a patient man, he'll put up with my huge size.

I'd escaped from Bridget and Alice, why did I still want

to know everything that went on between them? Can we ever stop cheating ourselves? Bridget's husband was out for Parliament, mine for the King – we had every reason not to speak to one another. Yet if I saw her coming, I'd meet her by chance. Not that either of us had much time to gossip: both had the work of two to get on with. But that streaming wet winter day when I found Bridget making the ground muddier yet with her tears, I did put my arms round her to comfort her.

I don't understand myself. Sometimes I try. Not often.

I knew what she was crying about. I'd been there – though I hadn't seen it. Thomas comes home from the war, he says: 'You don't see anything, in a battle. You remember in snatches.' So proud of himself, to have something to tell! I know now he was right, though I never told him so. Men aren't interested in women's chatter.

The way it went, one moment I was walking down the street, and thinking: Though your face stings with the cold, this weather, at least you don't sink into the mud. I was tired, I'd come from town, selling my wool. I had my money in a pouch between my breasts, I always keep money there. If anyone wants to poke for it, he's a brave man, with a longer reach than most.

The next moment the street was full of King's men and horses, and I thought: What's in my pack? Pins, nails, sewing thread – would they want that? Needy times, and the army, it seems, needier than any of us. A moment later, there were twice the number. The New Model Army had arrived. The captains were yelling at each other, masked as they were by their headgear; it was only later I knew they were the Smale lads, though I'd seen them God knows how many times, strutting about, boys first, then young men. And squabbling. This was their last falling-out.

The next minute bullets were flying, men jumping off their horses and firing from the poor beasts' flanks, using the animals for protection; now I thought, Jesus, I thought, Thomas isn't with the Smale lads, is he? I didn't know anything at that moment, only I didn't want to see him killed in front of my eyes. I saw the bright metal of the guns and the smoke puffing out, while the troopers were jarred by every shot they fired. And in spite of my moment's fear for Thomas, I didn't think they could harm me, till one of them threw his arms wide and sagged down to the ground, red spreading over him. Dead. And, Oh, Jesus, I thought, here I stand, as good a target as a haystack.

Now I remember myself up the side of Patience Morley's house, I don't know how I got there, and I grew thin in an instant, I swear. Wide and flat, I spread all over the wall, and the straw and horsehair poked out from the daub to scratch me. I wasn't alone for long. A trooper ran in beside me and began firing from the corner. And I couldn't move. I was pinned there. All I could do was slide a few steps further away from the street. The shots crashed in my ears, I closed my eyes and begged God's forgiveness for all my sins.

I can still hear the silence afterwards – it hurt, it was so quiet. It hurt worse when the trooper on the corner screamed. I guess he'd been screaming for longer, I hadn't heard him while they were fighting, he'd drawn breath in that moment of unbearable silence.

Thomas, I thought. Might it be Thomas? The man was bleeding and writhing and screaming, and his blood steamed on the cold ground. He was too big for Thomas. A moment later he gasped and lay still. And I couldn't move. I stayed there a week, I thought, before I could get out to see the bodies in the street. I was chilled to the bone, I was a cold shivering haystack now, shivering apart.

Thomas was right, you hardly see anything. Because I'd been up the side of Patience Morley's house (Bridget's crony, smiled on by Robert, another timid ninny). Inside the walls Patience, who was so anxious to see the fight she'd been peering out of the glass windows she was so proud of, had been shot dead.

I came out, and there was Bridget, who'd been with her – but *not* looking, not the way I knew Bridget – standing outside the house door, yammering: 'She's dead!'

'Cover her up, then,' I said, 'you fool.' And I ran off home on my shaking legs, thinking about the store cupboard. I'd hardly been busy twenty minutes before the King's troopers arrived. They didn't find everything I'd hidden.

I felt bad, I suppose, because I'd called her a fool. That was why I put my arms round her when I found her crying. She'd laid Patience out, smashed chest and all. Maybe that was why I thought she had more right to the horrors than I had, who never spoke about mine.

Her voice all wet and shaking, she said: 'I'm going to Mother, Margaret. I'm going to get a charm. To keep me safe and protect Robert from the enemy.'

I said: 'So that he can shoot my husband before my husband shoots him?'

She said: 'No, not that, of course not, how can you be so—'

She had a pretty soft face that smiled in spite of her, the way a baby smiles, to sweeten everyone.

I said: 'And from Mother – you know what Robert will think of that.'

She didn't care. She couldn't keep away from my mother, any more than I could. In spite of everything that had happened between them.

And so Bridget went to my mother and got the charm from her. Oh, she must have known Robert Tarry would beat her if he found out. Though before they were married he used Church money to pay Mother to find the Communion plate that was missing. He never forgave her for obliging him, was that it? So many questions! I can't stand it. Oh yes I can. I can stand anything. Big Margaret, solid as a rock and forever eating. When the times were lean, during the war, I had to chew bits of leather, my fingernails, the hard crusts no one wanted: they lasted for hours.

Bridget didn't want to be friends with my mother, she only wanted the charm. Safety, that was all she wanted. No, she wanted love. From the woman she'd been desperate to escape. Fool, I might say. No, I can't. Honesty has always been my downfall.

And Bridget stayed safe and sound, and Robert Tarry got home from the war. My mother was honest, too, in her own way. She gave value for money, my mother did.

HE SAID: 'Stop it.'

'Stop what? Let me sleep, that's all I want.'

'You'll sleep for ever, you hag, but I'll never be free of your laughter. Awkward Richard with his halting leg. You didn't believe it really hurt. It was broken, and you wouldn't set it. You said I was a fool to be so clumsy on the ice. I wouldn't be limping like this if it had been properly set.'

'I don't understand,' she said. 'That was the winter I was away. I came back, and they were talking about how you lamed yourself skating.'

'Don't make excuses. You didn't want to pay attention to me, did you?' Tears ran down his face and he groped for a handkerchief after all. 'And I was only ten. It hurt so badly.'

'Don't start snivelling,' she said, as he had known she would. 'I'll tell you something you ought to hear. About your churchwarden, Robert Tarry. What he did so that he could marry my Bridget and keep her.'

He sat back in his chair, listening, looking up at her.

'He had a gaming debt round his neck – that was the fruit of his pleasure at his first wife's death. He knew he was free, and thought he was lucky. So he staked everything he had on a cock. Of course, he lost. Never gamble when you're feeling lucky. Except you don't gamble money, do you? Can't even gamble ideas. Only happiness, that's what you stake, and recklessly. Well, there he stood, no money, desperate to have Bridget, convinced he ought to take her away from me. Since such a pious God-fearing man doesn't take any action without sanction from the Almighty, he prayed for a week before he decided to steal the money from the Church. There you are, that's something new for you. No, I'm not finished. Every day afterwards, when he was praying with his family, he thanked God for the especial blessing he had received. That was the money he stole. I've heard him at it.' She stretched her arms and clenched her fingers. He watched the movements, his head turning, the rest of him still. She said: 'And then, you know people think offertory money is lucky – that's paganism, you'll say. Yes. It knows the way into your church, no matter how tight you shut the door. Robert Tarry sells the coins at double their value, puts back as much as they're worth, and keeps the rest himself. He's always liked that parable about the talents, that tells how the Lord went away and told his servants to put his money to work and increase while he was gone. I suppose if the Lord came in person and demanded his money, Robert would give it all back to him. Only the Lord hasn't come yet. Lucky for Robert.'

She looked him over: he shifted in his chair. There was

something he needed to say. But he could hear Susan's pleading voice: 'One day these people will recognise your worth, Richard, believe me.' He had denied the pleading, and now the memory had become a taunt.

With difficulty, he said: 'You have a wicked tongue. I will not listen to slander.'

'Well, then,' she said, lewd amusement wrinkling up her old face. 'Did you ever hear the story of the man who lost his pizzle because a witch witched it away? She promised she'd give him back a better one, so she took him up the tallest tree in the village.'

I ought to silence her, he thought.

'There the pizzles hung,' she said, 'like leeches in waterweed. Jesus, it's hard for an old woman to stand all this time.'

'Ask yourself why you're standing there,' he said querulously.

She said: 'One of them was mighty big, so the hopeful lad asked if he could have it – with that in my breeches, thinks he, I could wreak havoc among the women. "Oh no," says the witch. "You can't have that one. That's our parson's."'

'You'll never let go of me,' he said, 'will you?'

She said: 'I'll be dead soon. You keep telling me so.'

He said: 'Your dog pissed on my leg. You laughed.'

CHAPTER SIX

ROBERT

I CAME back from the war on leave and she had the charm in the house. It was easy to find that out, because she wanted me to know what she'd done.

She had so many byways in her mind. She could have kept it secret. Did she want me to realise how much she loved me? Enough to take a talisman from that old hag?

'Robert, she's not human at all, she's a changeling, you know that, everyone knows that.' So Bridget said once – as if Alice were an outrage to an otherwise orderly family.

The light was yellow all round my wife, as she stood in the doorway watching me take my boots off; the dust danced in the glare. She had her head crooked to one side, which I used to find appealing. Then she came to crouch on the floor by my knee, her skirts picking up dirt. I made her get up. I had already kissed her; now I got up and walked all through the house, making sure everything was in place, checking the food stocks. It was wartime, and I'd had to replace the horse that had been shot down under me. I could allow no extravagance. She shadowed me, trotting at my heels.

I saw the charm as soon as I went up into the bedroom. She had it hanging by the bed, a piece of parchment tied up with a ribbon. I reached for it, and she smiled that guilty smile. She was pleased, I swear it.

I recognised the half-illiterate handwriting. Alice's. Alice had been sent to school long enough to scribble a few words and keep her accounts. If you make a woman learned, in never so small a degree, if you tame a fox – you make them both cunning. Alice was vixen enough.

I had to act.

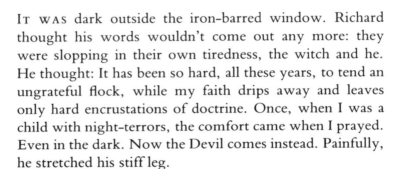

IT WAS dark outside the iron-barred window. Richard thought his words wouldn't come out any more: they were slopping in their own tiredness, the witch and he. He thought: It has been so hard, all these years, to tend an ungrateful flock, while my faith drips away and leaves only hard encrustations of doctrine. Once, when I was a child with night-terrors, the comfort came when I prayed. Even in the dark. Now the Devil comes instead. Painfully, he stretched his stiff leg.

The fiend said: 'Leave her be. Leave her to me. You're so tired. What does it matter? One more brand in the fire. And in any case,' the voice grew soft, caressed him, 'it isn't as you see it. Believe me. Though I am the Prince of Doubt.'

'How is it, then?' he demanded, turning on the tempter. The witch squinted at him in bewilderment. To her, he said angrily: 'You brought him.'

'Oh, no,' said Satan's velvet voice. '*You* brought me. As for your question, I am not here to supply answers.' The fiend settled himself in a corner of the cell, produced a roll of parchment, a pen and a bottle of ink, and began to write assiduously.

Richard slumped and dozed in his chair, waking with a start when he heard Alice muttering. He stood up and came close to her so that he could hear.

'It's soft, in the dark,' crooned Alice, 'warm and sweet, who needs a light? And if you go into the folds of shadow they are smudged silk, better than colour, cobweb-grey and shadow-black, charcoal, ebony, leading you into the dark you enter without names, you are not yet old enough for names—'

'Alice,' he scolded, slapping her sagging face. 'Wake up!'

Satan wheedled: 'Why must you wear yourself out, trying so hard?'

Alice's head straightened. Slurring her words, she asked: 'Did you ever hear the story, Your Reverence, of the lad who lost his pizzle because a witch witched it away? She promised him a better one, so she took him up a tree . . .'

RICHARD

AND DID even, in spite of the peril in which she stood, taunt me with the Devil's own lewdness, so I was forced to have her whipped.

MOTHER, she thought, come back and hold me. The way I held Bridget when she came running back to me, panting, her dress hanging on her back in tatters and covered with blood because Robert had laid about her with a horsewhip. She was shivering with cold. Mother, put your arms around me, Mother, wash my back. I never loved anyone but you, it was all a mistake. I only want you. Mother, kiss me to sleep in the warm. I don't know who I am.

I don't know anything any more.

I DON'T understand myself, thought Richard, why didn't I have her chained up again? And watching her moan and snivel on the floor, clutching her battered old body in her arms, he felt neither the satisfaction nor the justification some part of him had expected.

'You know who I am, don't you?' asked Satan. 'I am your dancing partner.'

'I don't understand you, fiend. And how should I know you so well?'

'When you move,' said Satan, 'I am designated to counter-move.'

Richard looked down at his feet and the floor was tiled with chequers: he stood on a white square, Satan on a black.

'Exactly,' said Satan. 'Only this game never ends. You knew, did you not, when you ordered her beaten, that you would cringe every time she was lashed?'

Richard said: 'I wanted her to know what it felt like.'

I *am* going mad, he thought. The words of the Witch-craft Act printed themselves large and black on the walls of the cell: so he read them off the stones, while Satan sat down on the furthest black square, closed his eyes and began to snore loudly.

'Or take up any dead man, woman, or child, out of his, her, or their grave, or any other place where the dead body resteth, to be employed or used in any manner of witchcraft, sorcery, charm, or enchantment.'

She said: 'The charm I gave Bridget. It wasn't what I said it was. It was written on a pig's skin.' As for the skull for the moss, she thought, I shan't talk about it unless he does, maybe he doesn't know.

Satan drew up his knees and blew out a sulphurous fart.

SARAH

BRIDGET was conceived in Ralfe Gibbons's house, which was draped with filmy cobwebs, the house where time changed as you stepped in through the door. People preferred to stay out of it, except when they went in on business. And even while I was Alice's best friend, I liked to meet her outdoors. Alice now, once she had set up in her own house, she was brisk and businesslike with her customers, but the hairs came up on the backs of their necks all the time. The grass grew thicker on the path to Alice's front door than it did on anyone else's. And lined with dark foxgloves in June. She had green and purple hellebores and black monkshood: all for her potions. Which she used for the seeming health of many, mine among the rest.

Did it smart when I taunted her with her questionable blood? I hope so. People had always thought she was a changeling – and with good reason. The fairy people might have stolen a Gibbons baby because it would take to their ways quicker than one that was all human. Or to remind the Gibbonses what they owed their forefathers. Ralfe was arrogant enough to need that reminder. They were all arrogant. And Alice, who didn't look like any of the rest of her family, puffed herself out with pride, as if to make up for her scrawny body.

The Little People are everywhere: forget to sweep your hearth and they'll turn your cream jar on its side to teach you a lesson. But they have their special places, and let no one tell me those aren't perilous. They were Alice's friends! For years, I envied her such grand company. Now look what's happened to Alice. I was better to stick to the simple pleasures, to my man and family, though the nap wears off love, and sons die or grow coarse and saddle you with coarser scolding daughters-in-law.

Bridget never wanted Alice's diversions, or her knowledge, and she was terrified of her mother's goblin friends.

That's how she was beguiled by sanctimonious Robert Tarry whose first wife had a face like a horse and a body as hot as a bitch in season. For most of their marriage, forgiving Robert was deprived of the chance to enjoy the heat for himself. Robert must have had a yearning for disaster, to follow Lisbeth with Bridget. And how was it everyone knew how he filched the Church money to clear his cock-fighting debt and marry her? It was all over the village within a week of the wedding. Alice, of course. She told her bees, to pay Robert Tarry for taking Bridget away. And who told Alice? It was Bridget. I can hardly blame her for that. The nights I've lain awake, digging out every confidence I ever gave Alice, laying them out in rows, persuading myself each one was harmless. Surely no one would hold it against me that I went with Martin before we were wed? Enough girls do it. Now I have other troubles. I am wet and cold and Audrey leaves great lumps of fat in the broth to turn my stomach. And I'm going to piss myself again.

Alice would come to Bridget's house, Bridget would frown and sigh at the sight of her mother, and half an hour later she was telling her all the gossip. She couldn't help herself. Alice's sharp comments pained her, for Bridget was easily shocked, eager to be proper and pure, the better to make herself a world Alice couldn't touch with her suspicious mind and lewd tongue. Bridget should have gone to live elsewhere if that was what she wanted. And she was never really one of us.

Audrey, you slattern, you lantern-jawed scold! I'll tell my son about you.

He'll take no notice. I am nothing, now I can't work any more. They don't throw me out, because that would disgrace them. No one comes near, except the Vicar, now Alice is gone, all my friends are dead. I can see Vicar wrinkle his well-born nose up because I smell so bad. I say, 'Audrey. It's her doing.' He tries to make my words out. Then he holds my hand, the better to keep his own away from his nostrils.

Alice was my friend, but for years I avoided her house. Then the day after they told me about Matthew – died a gallant death in battle, they said, as if that would comfort me – I didn't care where I was going, I was dizzy with pain, walking to get away from it. They gave up trying to stop me after an hour or so. I found myself at Alice's house. There stood Robert, he'd come to take Bridget back, I remembered how she'd been hiding at Alice's for a week, and I suppose Robert was tired of looking after the children. They were blocking the path, and none of them took any notice of me.

It felt as if I didn't exist, and I was glad of it. So I stood still and watched.

Robert and Alice were quarrelling at the door. Over Bridget, who was crying. 'I'll have her,' says Robert. 'No, I,' says Alice. Then Robert wants to know what was the charm Alice gave Bridget, and Alice said she'd written it on the skin of a dead baby.

She laughed in Robert's face when he flinched. She said his lucky escape from the cannonball had been her doing. Told him what he was most ashamed of, how he'd wet himself for fear, and his leathers had rubbed him raw by the time the battle was over. Told him he was too sore to straddle Bridget anyway, and she knew, she said, working herself into a rage, that was all he wanted of Bridget, so why didn't he leave her in peace?

Robert stood shaking, scared witless, and he shouted that she must have had the Devil's help to find that out, no one else knew it, where had she got it from? Because he hadn't even had time to tell Bridget – his wife wouldn't have been slow to let Alice know about it. Alice saw it in her silver bowl, or the tittering fairies told her, or she changed herself into some night-running creature, sneaked into Robert's house and saw him in his shirt.

But she'd gone too far, with the dead baby. Now Bridget was more frightened of her mother than she was of Robert. Bridget ran to Robert and clung to him, begged him to take her away, whimpering about faces – they leered at her, she said, in the dark. And Alice could see the loneliness opening at her feet again. I thought: Will she never learn?

I remember the two of them walking away down the path, Alice shouting after them that it was a pig's skin, a pig's skin, she'd only told Robert it was a baby's skin to torment him, didn't Bridget believe her?

I saw her face crumple, exposed and raw – and then I noticed that the sun cast no shadow behind her. Oh, God, I thought. She's a witch. And she hates me, she'll never love me again. All of a sudden, I wanted to live. A minute later, the sun was gone. I ran away myself, before she could see I was there.

'THE FAT of young children,' whispered Satan, running a finger down Richard's spine, 'that's what your books say they use, isn't it? They seethe it with water in a brazen vessel, reserving the thickest of that which remains boiled in the bottom, which they lay up and keep, till occasion serves to use it. They put to it eleoselinum, aconitum, and soot. They rub their skins therewith till they are exceedingly fiery and hot, fly up in the air and descend on whatever young lads take their fancy.'

My son, thought Richard. What did she do with my son's corpse?

'You believe it?' jeered Satan, drawing his sharp nail up to the nape of Richard's neck and ruffling one of his few remaining hairs. 'Did any witness say they saw Alice flying?'

MARGARET

BRIDGET came home from my mother's, all meek and mild and obedient to Robert, but as soon as he had gone back to the wars, she was off to Mother's cottage again. I was walking past on my way to the river with the clothes, and saw Judith meet her as my mother shut the door.

'What have you got in your hand, Bridget?' asked Judith, as if it was her business.

'Nothing,' said Bridget, casting her eyes down.

Judith knew, of course. Looked Bridget over, clicked her tongue, and went off to gossip about my little sister. She shouldn't think so highly of herself: I could tell a tale or two about her. I've seen her at market, short-changing foolish customers. And she had to use a love-charm herself, once. I got my man through nothing more than his love for me and my strong hard-working arms.

Bridget saw me, and ran to me. She told me her charm was written on a pig's skin. She wanted me to say I believed Mother. I wouldn't say anything. But she fretted at me till at last I said it must be a pig's skin. I had my washing to do, the butter to churn, the linen to weave, and the wood to chop for the fire. I told Bridget I was sure Mother wasn't lying. I don't know. Mother had dug by the gallows, to get her green-haired skull. Bridget knew that, and it was tormenting her now. But I could believe Mother had lied about the charm, to needle Robert. That was my mother. Truth, to her, was a tool to be used sparingly, when she thought it would be useful.

She could have kept the truth about the charm back, till she thought it would hurt her son-in-law. Who knows?

Mother, Bridget and I. It mattered to me what was behind every change in their voices and expressions, I wanted to read their thoughts. Mother could read most people's, and ours best of all. But Bridget – whatever she found out, she was skilled at shutting her eyes to it.

I knew my mother really hated me, and when I was old enough, I spared no effort to make her admit it.

Honesty has always been my downfall.

'ALICE', said Richard. 'Is it true that you wrote the charm on a pig's skin?'

'It was a pig's skin.'

'That must be a lie,' he insisted, lusting for misery. 'Alice, I can have you whipped again for your obstinacy. I will have them run you for an hour this time, Alice.' She looked up blearily from the huddle of her old limbs on the filthy floor. Foolishly, he thought: The chessboard has vanished. 'Hell gapes, Alice,' he said. 'Now is the time to tell the truth and shame the Devil.' Shameless Satan laughed, as Richard had known he would.

'I'm not lying,' she said. 'Why don't you want to believe me?' She thought: He needs to be convinced.

'And my son, Alice, did you let him lie quiet in his grave?' Tears jarred his voice again.

She thought: Now I have him. I can torment him, can say I dug his son up, roasted his sweetbreads for my dinner, gave the liver and lights to my dog. He wants a confession, doesn't he, isn't that why he won't let me sleep? He'd never have another night's sleep himself.

She looked at his long thin face that stretched up into the bald scalp, at his eyebrows raised against the weight of melancholy and fear: I can't, she thought, I'm sorry for him. Why am I sorry for him, when he had me beaten?

She said: 'I never touched your son.'

Relief ran through him.

He said: 'I believe you, Alice. But you must forgive me this. I cannot let you lie in the same churchyard as my little child.'

She shrugged her shoulders.

SIMON

THAT MORNING the mist lay in the air like milk in water, can't get drunk on milk, here I am, poor rat-catcher, sober as the devil. Milk in water, and the trees stood out of it, under the trees you fumbled your way, but if you climbed a hill to look for the King's men, you could see the bare black branches fingering out of the whiteness. Cold it was. Cold as steel (but a cannonball, that's hot). There came another detachment of troopers, our men, New Model men. Righteous and stern. Only drunk with ideas. Diggers, Ranters, Levellers, Anabaptists. New Model hodgepodge.

The fear of the Lord and the desire for justice – or just the sickening feel of terror in your guts, you think you'll never be able to move, when you do move there's still something cowering in you, keep quite still, they might not notice you.

There was Robert Tarry, in charge of the troopers. So it was: 'Robert! The Lord sent you here!' and – more anxiously, this: 'Have you been home?'

Courageous for the Lord is one thing, but who has the courage to wonder who your wife is carrying on with, behind your back? I had no such doubts, I knew my little wantons would be bedding as many men as they could fit between their legs. That's why I wouldn't have chosen to leave them.

Robert began boasting that he'd put paid to Alice's plots, how she'd foisted a charm on Bridget that was made with the skin of a dead baby. My own skin crawled. Hadn't my mother always known, and no one paid attention to her? And he said: 'Henry Tidbury, I swear to you, I saw her standing there in the bright sunlight, and she cast no shadow. It's as true as I stand here, Henry.'

So then it was down on their knees, and 'Down on your knees!' to me. I wasn't sorry to join them. They read from the Bible and we all bowed our heads in hope. It was the same when you went into battle: that was the moment for faith. Even though I'd seen scores of men pray fervently, only to be smashed by the guns and trampled by Rupert's horse. You have to have something to get you through.

And indeed, we all felt better, safer, brushed the dirt off our knees and stood up straight, like men. And Corporal Henry Tidbury, who'd had me flogged for getting a girl pregnant, he said: 'We settle her, when we get home. She's troubled my mother enough – it'll be a pleasure.' Ah, but the last I saw of Corporal Henry Tidbury, he was a red mess on the field at Naseby. Half an hour later, I was struck down. They said I was lucky to survive. Did the witch kill Corporal Tidbury, did she direct the musket shot that wrecked my face and send the horse to trample my arm?

Robert came home safe, thanks to the charm we all know about, till his wife offended her mother. Now he has neither wife nor children. But Jesus said his kingdom wasn't of this world. To ram the point home, the Army never paid me, they said God prospers the righteous, does that cut me out? They gave me one thing that felt good.

They gave me orders to lead my horse into a church, once, twice, time and again, to tie the brute up to dung what Parson calls the sanctuary, and fire my musket at all the windows. Lying thieves, smooth and confident in their black robes – even our Vicar, though his gait would make you think him as drunk as I am – I spoiled their house for them. They should all be set loose on the roads to earn their living catching rats.

If God prospers the righteous, then the righteous – and God – are in league with the Devil. For all the land Alice inherited when her husband, my half-uncle Francis, died, the land Robert Tarry has set his fat hands on because big Margaret's run off, ought to belong to me. If Alice hadn't killed my father, if that hypocrite Sykes hadn't stopped my parents marrying before I was born. But no one ever thinks of me, except to curse me.

ALICE said: 'I don't care where they shovel me away. I'll be free.' She thought: I don't know what I'm saying any more.

'I know how to escape,' she said to Richard. 'I used to turn myself into a hare. Those nights when the moon's full and the trees throw black shadows on the fields. I'd feel hair growing on my skin, I was shrinking, but my legs grew powerful and swift, and I'd run out to the other creatures of the night. I never made men into clumsy horses, my own legs were better. I didn't go smelling out the fusty village secrets. There were other hares to run with, yes, and couple with, too. I'd jump and dance, and dodge the weasels through the long grass. Then I'd stay quite still, because the owl was overhead, even my whiskers froze – if he'd swooped, though, I'd have sent him about his business. He'd have known me. I ran faster than the wind, there was nothing I couldn't have raced, I was drunk with the scent of elder blossom.'

He said: 'It wasn't so.'

'No,' she agreed. 'Let me tell it another way. I made myself into a weasel and slipped into every house: I listened to the secrets that were told in every bed, I ran over my neighbours while they slept, lifted the covers, saw their spots and blemishes, and bit their ears to give them bad dreams. If any of them had specially offended me, I blocked their mouths and noses with my body till they fought for breath, then I let go of them, only to torment them again when they had fallen quiet. I pissed in their cream to spoil the butter, and in their beer to turn it sour. Now, you'll say, the truth is out. Won't you?'

He was silent.

'Say it,' urged taunting Satan. 'Why not?'

CHAPTER SEVEN

JUDITH

ONCE ALICE turned vicious, at least she was out in the open: you knew you had to beware of her.

But before that, we all ran to her – except the Parson, and he turned his eyes away, about his precious Communion cup – 'Oh, Alice, can you help me, my arm's been hurting for days now, Alice, I've lost my half a dozen silver pieces, my life's savings, tell me who stole them, Alice, I'm sure someone's laid a spell on me, Alice, I want to know if I'll marry the boy I love, give me a charm to make sure, Alice, my leg's stiff, Alice, this child won't talk, walk—'

Alice would smile, invite us in, and spend an hour with us. She set bones, she took the murrain off cattle, she tied up bits of this and pieces of that for us, and we hung them round our necks. They worked. She treated us like her favourite children, while we were with her, and we prattled our secrets to her. She charged us according to our means, which meant the poorest paid nothing. Nobody ever believed in the Church the way we believed in Alice. We didn't understand either the Church service or what she was doing, but she gave us something to take away with us, she touched us and listened to us without preaching.

And stole the marrow of our own selves for her own purposes.

Peter Gough went to her, claiming someone had stolen

his scythe. She laughed in his face and told him about all the petty thieving he'd done: who'd crept into her own house and stolen a purse once? she asked him. Peter Gough, you owe more than the worth of a scythe. He shouted at her, you could hear him all over the village, but she smiled, wouldn't budge, and asked for her pay. He gave it to her. That kept her in favour with the rest of us.

AND BRIDGET, turning in her grave underneath Alice, moans: 'I want to grow up, I want to grow up. All I ever wanted was to be safe. I thought Robert would help me, he said prayer would banish the squeaking goblins who came round my bed with their gleaming undead eyes and their greedy fingers. I thought he could stop the worms turning into poisonous snakes when I worked in the garden, I thought he could save my feet from walking towards fairy rings on St John's Eve. I'd forget the things that moved in Mother's silver bowl, the shapes that shone inside my hands when I put them over my eyes, the voices that spoke inside my head, teaching me a story I didn't want to listen to, but where can you stop the ears inside your head? He couldn't do it. It was Mother – who thought me a clumsy coward, though it was years before she said it aloud – she fended them off with charms and spells, maybe her patience ran out, for one day her remedies failed me too. Now it's too late, I want to find a way to do it myself. I want to grow up. I want to grow up.'

And: 'Bridget!' cries Robert Tarry in his own grave, the mound of which has been levelled so that the parish can run a hover mower over the grass. Robert's exemplary third wife starts in outrage from her own rest, to hear him address her disgraceful rival.

Robert thinks of Bridget's white limbs, her soft breasts and belly. His senses revive and tantalise him with the sweetness of that body, the comfort of his entry into it, the pleasure of her lips, her legs, moving with his.

But the birch tree that haunts the other side of the churchyard wall, its fingers groping into sanctified ground, moves in the wind, and whispers: 'I have you, there is none of all that left. I have eaten and drunk your sap, and you are dry now, so sleep, it is no longer the time to want, sleep, your bones and your skull are empty, only the ashes of words lie round them. Sleep, sleep,' whispers the birch tree in the wind. 'Sleep. It is a horror for you to be awake.'

And the voices fade away. An owl hoots, and a cat hunts across the graves.

ALICE SAID to Richard: 'Your wife came to me once. She said her arm hurt her, so I stroked it better and gave her a salve.'

Devils, he thought. There are devils everywhere. I am visited by Satan, but there is Belial, there is Lucifer, there is Beelzebub. There are incubi that enter women in the night, and succubi that draw men's seed from them: Alice, he thought, was maybe conceived of an incubus, and who or what might have been the father of my dead son who lies in hallowed ground? Shrinking, he saw them all for a moment, the air was alive with demons, even the smallest had gross leering faces and clung to the ceiling of the cell like so many bats. Their wings flapped in his eyes: he had to push them apart with his hands. Alice was still talking.

'Then, just as she was about to go, she turned on the doorstep and asked me for a charm.' Alice paused and watched his face with a mixture of concern and malicious knowingness in her bleared eyes. 'She wanted a charm to make you believe she loved you.'

And what, he thought, does that mean?'

'She was distracted with it,' said Alice, 'that was what made her arm ache so she could hardly move it, she was at her wits' end with trying to persuade you. She wept all over my shoulder. I made her sit down and gave her a posset to calm her, and put the charm up for her. But she came back a month later and said it didn't work. She wanted her money back from me.'

He thought: Now I know why it was Susan who died.

'She said she had to account to you for every penny she spent: she was lying. Wasn't she?'

'Yes,' he said, and thought: I am a traitor.

Alice said: 'It couldn't work on you, could it? There were always some things even my skill couldn't do. I gave her the money back. She told me how wicked it had been of her to consult me, she stood there with a pleading expression on her silly face, maybe she thought if she insulted me enough I might forgive her. She needed someone's forgiveness. She wronged you by being pretty while you were plain, and you never forgave her, did you?'

Miserably, he said: 'Sir Thomas used to come, when I was out supervising the work on the land, or visiting. He always came when I was out.' A small devil swooped down to sit gesturing on his shoulder. 'Didn't he have a reason to come at those times? He would sit talking to Susan, they would smile at each other, he sent her letters with poems he had written out – poems from a grocer. Do you think I don't recognise tenderness? What else did they do together?'

Satan was writing: 'The cleric's sin, no question of it, was, that though his wife was good and virtuous, he did constantly suspect her, but dared not challenge her out-right with the infidelity he had fabricated—'

A tiny tumbling fiend brushed Satan's hand and the ink spurted over the page and onto the straw. Satan, in irritation, waved his arms and the whole flock of them disappeared. Satan wrote again – the words came out on both sides of the paper, Richard could see them clearly.

'But dared not challenge his wife outright with the infidelity he fabricated against her, preferring to nourish in the vapours of his mind the allegation that she could not love him. What folly! Did she not give him children? She was obedient and hard-working, and had a sweet tongue. Should that not have been enough for him?'

'No,' said Richard.

'I don't know,' said Alice. 'I don't know about your wife and Sir Thomas.'

Like a bleak cold emptiness, the memory of Bridget came to torment her hungry belly. She said quickly: 'Was there anything else you wanted to know?'

MARGARET

IT's A long road, to London. The inns are lousy, and you sleep ten to a bed. We'll find work in the city, Thomas says. Doing what?

My thoughts run like a caged squirrel, more busily than my feet have been walking. Memories jig about like branches in a high wind, you can't fix them with your eyes, they puzzle and tease. What were they like, my mother and my foster-sister? I can't see their faces now. All I can see is their movements.

Bridget, she moved deftly, tightly, her hands patted, she set her feet down neatly. Only sometimes she'd trip over something or drop something, then freeze, for there was the egg smashed, the plate or tankard dented, her pretty legs were bruised and a stool had been sent flying across the room – and it shouldn't have been Mother she was afraid of, and it wasn't entirely. If I startled Bridget, her hands would clutch: her sides, her mouth, her hair, even me.

Quick, that was my mother. Quick to slap me, and it stung. If I bawled, she'd tire of the noise as quickly and shove a piece of bread, or cake, or honeycomb into my mouth. Done with now. Stop your bawling. When I was older, I'd swallow the titbit, and spit the crumbs on her feet. Her hand would answer me. Then one day, I thought: I'm bigger than her. If she slaps me, I can slap her back. I didn't. I cried badly that time, I thought I'd never stop.

Whatever she talked about, whatever thing, whatever place, whatever person, her voice took possession of it. It was never the same again. I tried never to talk to her about Thomas. She staked out a few pieces of him, all the same, with her bad tongue, 'not much of a man' bit the worst. How could I find any man who had more bulk than I had? I try to spit the poison out, when it rises in my throat. But if you've lived for years with that kind of mother, there's little enough you can call your own. Lucky I don't know where she went when she ran away from the village. Maybe she went to London. Maybe not. She didn't lay her tongue on it, that's good enough for me.

Her hands were soft, on Bridget. But I'm tough, I've never needed gentleness.

Mother did have gentleness. Patience, too. For the bees, for the calving cow, for the seedlings, for the picture forming in the silver bowl. And she waited patiently for Bridget to admit she saw the picture too. Only Bridget never admitted it. I wanted to see something, wanted to give the picture to my mother, then maybe she'd leave me something of my own in exchange. But I really didn't see anything, and she slapped me. I think Bridget would rather have been slapped than endure Mother's patient waiting. That was Bridget's punishment.

JUDITH

I LAUGHED about it, when it happened. I laughed and didn't understand why I was laughing. I never went to Alice again. Too frightened. Yes, even I, and it takes something really bad to frighten me.

Even t'other wisewoman couldn't persuade me Alice's hold on me was gone. I went to her for release, but a voice inside my head said: Don't tell her too much, she's like Alice, however different she may look, they're marked with the same mark. So I never told her – or anyone – about this. Now I think I should have done.

I can hardly bear to tell it even inside my own head.

It's not like me to brood. I've enough to keep my thoughts occupied, always so much work, and the accounts waiting to be tallied. Churning's hard enough work – you shouldn't be able to think while you're doing it. Slap, slap, the paddle heaves the cream about. My muscles work and ache. I tell myself: I'm a tall strong woman. I'm well respected in the village. I do my hair neatly and make my clothes well, my caps are always white and crisp. The flowers in my garden grow as they're meant to and smile up at me like good children. And if there are one or two small things I keep to myself, whose business is that? If people are fools enough not to count their change, for one – let them come back and tell me I haven't given them enough; then I'm always terribly sorry and I set it right at once. And how many women haven't fetched themselves a love-charm to fix their sweetheart's affections?

Only the woman I got it from was Alice.

She sent me away, she told me to come back in three days' time, she liked to do that, it made more mystery. I waited, and came back. What was strange about Alice's house, always so clean in those days – she even kept her chickens outside – you ducked away from the cobwebs. They weren't there.

She watched me come in, she saw me swallow hard for fear, and I saw her quick, secret smile. Even today, when she had other things on her mind. Though I didn't know, Bridget had agreed to wed Robert Tarry.

I suppose, when Margaret married Thomas, Alice was glad to get her out of the house. Alice hated her own daughter. Though Margaret was a good worker, and so strong she could have picked her little husband up and carried him away under her arm – how we laughed, behind our hands, at the wedding, and she knew, and kept her face dour. And Margaret was afraid of Thomas! Oh, she was full of fears, for all she pretended the opposite. Whenever Alice spoke to her, you could see her whole body cringe.

I'd have been glad, if I'd heard about Robert and Bridget. I might even have done without the love-charm. For Bridget, who hardly ever went out, was a sort of dream for all the village boys, everyone's rival, a lovely face glimpsed once or twice a week, a wonder, and more enticing since all their mothers had warned them off her because her parentage was so unnatural. Now the old women have been proved right, and the staid men look at their solid wives and congratulate themselves. But maybe feel a twinge of longing, too? Even John? Who knows.

Robert's mother was dead, but his own experience

might have warned him. Yet Bridget was so different from his first wife, so timid, so obedient, so virtuous. You couldn't quarrel with any of that. Oh, you have to pick a careful path, in life. There are pitfalls and mantraps everywhere.

'So it's you,' said Alice to me with that small pleased smile. 'My dear,' she went on, sweeter than sugar. 'Just stay here with Bridget,' she said, 'and I'll get your charm.'

I tried to greet Bridget, but she took no notice of me. She was sitting on a stool, twirling a spindle with no wool on it. Her face was as empty as the spindle. I found myself backing away, and I forgot to dodge a cobweb. I'll swear it brushed my face, soft and old, and the dust got into my throat and set me coughing.

There was neither cobweb nor dust.

Alice's good-for-nothing Francis was bedridden by then, and my coughing started him off in the other room. Bridget put her hands over her ears as if the noise was too much for her. And one of Francis's coughs turned into a yelp, and then a scream. Like slaughter.

In he came, running as best he could, tripping over his trailing blanket, gibbering, there's a black weasel in his room, he said, red eyes like coals, it went for his throat, he said, and he only just got away, then: 'Oh, God help me, it's here!'

I saw it.

'Alice!' I cried out. 'Alice, come and help us!' and Bridget laughed like a madwoman. That was what shook me the worst, her laughter. It came to me that you couldn't hear Alice moving about, not anywhere. The weasel was sitting on Francis's jittering shoulders, and it turned and fixed me with its eyes. Its eyes were green, not red. It was on Francis's head, nipping him, plaguing him, teasing him and terrifying him, it blinded his eyes with its tail and he missed his footing and crashed down on the floor. Then it got at his throat.

Bridget fell down on her knees beside Francis, trying to get it off him. It fastened on her wrist – I saw the blood – and then it was at her neck, as if it would burrow down under her kerchief. Francis rolled over, trying to get up, his knees went down and his naked flabby bum went up in the air. I found myself laughing the way Bridget had done, the laughter tore out of me and my heart went thud – thud – like a mallet against my chest, but to see Francis's behind poking like a white sugarloaf—

And suddenly, Alice was there.

To me, she said: 'What are you laughing at?' To Bridget: 'Get him back to bed.' Francis was panting as Bridget helped him up. Bridget's teeth were chattering.

I stopped laughing.

'Here you are,' said Alice to me, and again, she said: 'my dear. I wish you joy of him and what he keeps in his breeches,' she smiled as if nothing had happened, 'and if you put this between your breasts you'll see how well he goes to work with you, and if his pizzle has been dipped in wine, it should be the sweeter for it.'

Bridget came back, still shaking, and Alice put her arm round her. She said: 'Bridget, sweetheart, your wrist's bleeding.'

I'll never forget the way Bridget huddled inside Alice's arms, as if she was trying to shrink in on herself, away from her mother's flesh, and huge shudders ran through her, you thought she'd never stop.

Every time I saw John naked, I thought Alice's greedy eye had been on that part of him. Maybe she'd even put the winestain there?

She's dead now. Finished, powerless at last, with the stones landing on her grave.

SARAH

SHE HADN'T spoken to me, for years she'd behaved as if I didn't exist any more, but she was beside herself that day, usually she had such a secret way with her, like a cat that squalls suddenly and slashes you with its claws, then begins to purr again. That was the only day I really saw Alice behave just like the rest of us. Distraught, looking for someone to pour it all out to, and the person she met, at the well, was Sarah. Even Sarah would do.

'She's breaking everything,' she cried, 'she's wrecking all I have, then she'll want me to give her something to take with her to his house. I can tell you, Sarah, you're lucky to have no daughters, they break your heart and your crocks.'

When Bridget took her first steps, Alice walked her half-way round the village, holding her hands, so proud you'd think she'd just learned to walk herself.

Alice laughed. Her laughter tore me. I didn't want to hurt for her, but I put my hand on her arm. She stayed still, as if my touch comforted her. Now, I thought, it's happening. We'll be friends again, and she'll have learned what she may have of me and what she can't expect. While my flesh knew her touch down to the core of me – there are some things you never forget.

I asked: 'Bridget?'

'Who else could I mean?' She moved, and pulled her bucket up awkwardly, the way I'd never seen her before; it went sideways and the water splashed all over her feet. Alice screeched with rage, then with laughter again.

'What did I tell you?' she demanded. She hooked the bucket onto the rope again, and let it down. She turned her back on me.

'Alice,' I said. 'Alice, aren't you lonely? Can't you let me comfort you, Alice?'

Her thin back stiffened. I was beside myself. I said: 'Alice, I'm your friend, believe me, I'll make it up to you, I'm sorry. Alice.' I even said: 'Alice, I love you.'

She walked away and left me with my shame.

MARGARET

As soon as I got out of that house, Bridget and my mother were at each other's throats. Now they didn't have me to blame for everything that went wrong, so they savaged each other. Oh, there was as much spite hidden in Bridget's shivering silly virtue as there was in Alice's few inches of poison.

My father grew weaker by the day, not that anyone cared or they might have begun asking the sort of questions they asked when old Sarah was lamed – but he'd made precious little in his life, except a goodly stock of enemies. The things in the house started to break of their own accord. I saw it, when I visited. I'd be standing there and a pot would hop off its hook and all but brain me. The herbs my mother hung from the ceiling to dry would burst into flames and fall on the floor like a bunch of fiery flowers – it only ever happened when Bridget and my mother were there together, or the house would have burned down. Once the big stewpot cracked loudly and fell in two pieces: the dinner, which was cooking in it, slopped and hissed onto the fire, blackening and stinking and smoking us out of the door. And birds would get in and flap crazily against the walls, never managing to escape. They always died of fright, and my mother, who was never one to waste anything, put them in pies.

She tried to get me to take a blackbird home once, but I wouldn't. Its open eyes looked curses at me. I wasn't going to pluck that creature's feathers and draw its guts out, not in the name of any thrift on earth.

Three weeks after Bridget's wedding – shall I ever forget my mother's face that day? She smiled as if she'd always wanted this marriage – my father died. I suppose there was so much poison in the house, and only one feeble man left to be dosed with it.

CHAPTER EIGHT

SIMON

IF I'M a sot, a good-for-nothing rat-catcher and a filthy pedlar of remedies against the French pox – a cheat, some say – it's Alice's fault. So my mother said. But my mother said a lot. She never stopped. Most of the time, her customers weren't listening.

She used to talk about Alice, because she hated her. Everyone knew why. Alice was sitting on land that should have been ours – while my mother was forced to sell ale for a living, though since she drank half of it herself, she was usually in debt, so you couldn't call it a living.

'She'll end in hell,' said my mother, pulling at her ale. I was sitting too far away from the fire, and the cold came up behind and put its arms round me. Oh, no, I'd think. Alice again.

'Why do they leave her be?' my mother wanted to know. 'She should have been hanged years ago, they can hang people, you know, for doing what she does, finding lost property, selling love-charms, telling fortunes, my lawyer told me,' said she, as if she was my lady Berkeley. And everyone knew, even I knew, though I wasn't born at the time, that her lawyer had run off with all her money, and left her only this scrap of fodder for her spite. So the customers looked at the floor, waiting for her to finish. I was angry with them, and ashamed of her. I wanted to go out before she began talking about me, only I didn't like it in the cold dark. So I stayed.

For every cup of ale she poured out, she drank one herself, while most of her customers, thrifty folk, made their portion last the evening. And if they'd been more spendthrift, she'd have died sooner. I owe my drunken mother's longer life to this village's sobriety.

Said she: 'Here I am, working away, my son, lazy lump, never moves a finger, he should be the staff to my old age, and his father was a good man, but Alice Slade spoiled my son,' she said, 'once when my back was turned she fed him an apple. He was only four years old,' she began sobbing as usual, 'and I'd gone to milk the cow and there he stood with that evil creature lowering over him, and half of it already down his throat. I held him upside down,' she said, 'but the apple wouldn't jump out, all the purges I tried did nothing, he wouldn't vomit, though I dosed him so strongly his bowels should have come up through his mouth.' She shook her head, and some of her drink spilled out sideways. We were burning wood I'd stolen – Tidbury's old wagon that had fallen apart – and something flared up white and green and lit her back. Her shadow wobbled like the flames – she was almost ready to fall in a drunken heap. The men either side of her got ready to catch her. She staggered backwards and they pulled her away from the fire. And they looked at me, as they always did. I hated it.

I can't remember Alice Slade giving me an apple, though I won't eat apples, so maybe there's some truth in it. I'm Alice's creature, then, poor drunken hideous sinner. Defiled for ever.

My mother said: 'I saw Alice ride her husband, poor Francis, across the fields in the snow. My son's drunken uncle Francis,' she said, rubbing my nose in it. 'My poor bastard boy,' she said to me. 'I'd been up with the cow,' (you'd think they'd begged her for the story). 'I saw Alice Slade flying across the fields, the horse had Francis's face, and there was red foam round the bit, it was trying to get free of her, but she held its head straight and scored its sides with a pair of spurs that were white-tipped as if they'd been pulled out of the smithy furnace.'

Someone asked her: 'How much had you had to drink?'

They laughed, as if laughter made them safe. My mother toppled for the night. I knew I'd have to finish all the work. And get her to bed afterwards. I thought: 'If I was a man, I'd teach them to laugh at my mother. If I was half a man, now. I sat still. The half of me that loved her wanted to fight, but the other half hated her, and kept all of me still in a cold corner.

We'd lie together in bed, and she'd wake up and say: 'None of them believe me. You believe me, don't you?' and I'd say, 'Yes, Mother.' The rats ran across the floor, and the hungry dark lay in wait just beyond the bed-curtains. I shivered with fear of it. Then one night: 'Out of my bed,' said she, jerking me out of a dream, 'the filth you've made in it, if you're a man now, you can sleep on the floor till you make yourself a new bed.'

'Mother,' said I, in tears, clinging to her, 'don't push me out into the dark.'

'Take your hands off me,' she said, 'you lusting lump.' Turned over and snored. It wasn't long before I found younger women's bodies to get close to, and they didn't mind my hands on them, not in those days. I had a pretty face, then. But always, always, afraid of the dark.

'You killed Dad,' Bridget accuses Alice as they lie among the bony flints and hard lumps of clay, and their hostilities writhe and coil about each other in the subsoil.

'He wasn't your dad,' snaps Alice.

'Oh,' says Bridget, 'you want to take everything away from me. You weren't my mother, but I always gave you the name. You hated him the way you hated me. He loved me. I was good to him. He was glad of what I gave him. But I could never give you what you wanted. Why were you a hypocrite, when he died? Why did you cry, even for five minutes? I never saw you cry over his illness, when he was alive.'

Alice, sharply: 'I don't have to account to you for my weeping, or my dry eyes. I suffered enough at that man's hands. You know nothing, you fool. You have nothing to say. All the years before you were born, my back was raw every night, and other parts of me, too. You came snivelling to me after one beating, but if I'd run to my father, he'd have whipped me himself and sent me back.'

And Bridget, as always, is silenced, and tries to escape. She can't, not now. Margaret has thrown them together for ever while she walks away. A mother's hatred (thinks Bridget) might be better than her love.

Bridget cries: 'Love is a sweet sticky trap, and it has limed my soul. It is love keeps me prisoner, not the weight of another corpse, or six feet of clay.'

The three dead boys sleep soundly, undisturbed by the quarrel.

'I was harmless, really,' Alice whined and wheedled, her face on her arm. 'I couldn't help it when my skill failed me, as for Francis, they don't understand, when he died he hadn't beaten me for years, and I missed him when he wasn't there picking spiders off himself, you get used to burdens, your back shapes itself to them and when the burden goes, you ache again. Nobody understands. You can forgive the present, it's harder to let go of the past. And Bridget – I did love her, I didn't send her away when she came for my help, I did my best for her, I was patient with her, she turned against me, I don't understand why. No one wants you when you get old, no one does you justice. And I want a pie, my stomach's girning for it, and Richard Berkeley won't give it to me, I want to sleep and he keeps shaking me awake, what's all this trouble for, I don't know?'

The Devil wrote: At times wonderfully lucid, sometimes so deranged you would say they should send her to Bedlam hospital rather than hanging her. It is less trouble to hang her.

Richard knew he should answer Alice. Salvation, he could say, is what the trouble is for. He said nothing.

JAMES SYKES

I CAME back to the village through wet falling sleet, my fingers and toes so numb I thought I'd lost them. When they turned me out of prison, I began walking, and came back to Whitchurch St Leonard, though I neither intended to go there nor knew I was there when I arrived. My feet were wiser than my head. The cold wind burned the raw scars where my ears had been. I found the outermost house in the village: it was hers. I fell in a heap on the doorstep. She opened up to see what the noise was.

The next thing I knew I was inside, by the fire, she had taken my wet clothes off me and wrapped me in a blanket. She sat beside me, stroking my back and crooning to me. I wept. For as long as I needed. She fed me and gave me a posset of herbs. I let myself be weak, under her hand.

I already loved her, but had thought my love was evil, thought she was evil. Now I knew better. I still thought the love should remain (as I then saw it) pure. I had opened to the Light, in prison, and was less accessible to the lies of those in authority. Yet I was still half enslaved to the Book.

SARAH

SHE WAS a witch. No need for the words: 'Who was she?' to ring and hurt in my head. But if you lie all day in fog and your own filth, you ask yourself all sorts of crazy questions. Such as: 'Who am I, now my looks have gone?'

No longer handsome Sarah with her bright eyes and sweet voice, I am ugly Sarah, nothing Sarah. I squealed when Audrey pulled at the knots in my hair, so now she's stopped combing it: the mice are nesting in there for all I know, it itches enough.

Alice said she wanted the dark. I hope she has enough of it now. But Sarah's on a cliff-edge over darkness, half of me has toppled already, and wants to take the other half with it.

Alice is there, trying to push me over.

JUDITH

ALICE WAS a witch. We all know that. She had a poisonous glare, a wicked tongue, she was ugly, and we were afraid of her. Which proved how crazy Sykes is, who seemed to think she had the key to some kind of holy secret.

JAMES SYKES

BRIDGET, her adopted daughter, who was her niece, and, if appearances did not lie, her half-sister as well, was a feeble bundle of nerves, useless, I suspect, even in bed, for all she bore Robert Tarry three children. But how easily those three boys died, how easily Bridget died! Which was none of it Alice's fault.

Francis Slade's seed was too rotten to come to life in Alice more than once, and was so full of contagion that she was always grievously sick after giving birth to his rotting offspring. It was pity for her weakness had watered the ground for my love of her. The struggle against love wrenched the sinews of my will and seared my heart, for I was obliged to hate her, as of my office. But I hated all womankind.

Enslaved to the cruel words of Paul of Tarsus, who scorned all bodily pleasure, I would not spill my seed anywhere, and spent hours on my knees in the church, did I find the evidence of sleeping desire. I deceived myself that this was evidence of demonic powers in the world. And so I lived in loneliness and great confusion of spirit, convinced of sin and impatient for the Last Day. I searched the Scriptures to find reference to the events of the moment, and made my worthless treasures into sermons for my parishioners. Who being wiser than I, used the time to sleep and rest from their labours.

The powers that be, said the Apostle, are ordained of God. The Church commands us to believe it. I doubt it. I doubt everything but what I have experienced for myself, and there is such a light there, such wonder!

Alice was good, as I am good. Those who inflicted such savage and harsh punishment on us, they are not evil, but in the dark, clutching and groping and doing blind damage.

★

'ALICE,' said Richard, as he might have said, Mother.

'I'm so tired,' she said, 'but I suppose you won't let me alone. Ask me.'

'The sabbat,' he said. 'In Germany, in France, in Scotland, they say witches go to dance with Satan and—'

'You could ask *me* that,' said Satan. 'But would you believe the answer?'

She said: 'Who else would I dance with? That fool wisewoman over at Whitchurch St Michael? No – I'll tell you this. I went to dance with the fairies, on St John's Eve you can go inside their hill. And eat their food, it's good food—' a dribble ran out of the corner of her mouth and she spat it onto the floor. Some of the spittle hit Richard's offended foot. 'Apples,' she said. 'And cherries and plums, all sweet and moist, that's what they like. Apricots. And almond paste, and honey cakes. Sweet pies.' She put her head on her knee: he shook her. She complained: 'Are you still there?'

'Describe the fairies' houses.' As he might have said, Mother, tell me a story.

Her old voice was sleepy, wobbly, resigned: 'The walls of their caverns are lined with yellow silk, and they wear silk, poppy-scarlet and larkspur-blue. Their dishes are gold and silver.'

The bell tolled twice outside. It rang on in Richard's head, and he saw colours in a church, windows glowing with red and yellow, blue and green, precious gold-stitched cloths on the altar, embellished by vessels of silver. He heard music, and prayers in a language whose beauty sang in him like desire. And the taste of God on his tongue: This is my Body. Why, he thought, do they want to take the colour away? My church is empty now. Do I care about these things because I am a child, listening to stories and songs, looking at pictures, does the child know something precious?

He thought: I moved in the church like a dancer, the grace of my service freed me from clumsiness.

He said to Alice: 'Tell me more.'

She said: 'When they hold their great feasts, they wear animal heads. You see antlers, and waving trunks, and horns coming up from their snouts, you're brushed by long hair, you feel warm dog-breath on the back of your neck. It feels good, the little shiver down your spine.'

'Why do they take that shape?'

'They do nothing too seriously, they don't feel the way we do. It's pleasurable: that's all they need to know. They're strict, above ground, with housewives, they punish untidiness and reward thrift and hard work, but down there they toss the stones of their fruits on the floor, they leave the crusts of pies, they spit out anything they don't find sweet enough. It's not important, down there. Because if you crinkle your eyes up, you see they're dressed in dry leaves, and the furniture is made of old dead bones. So you don't squint: it's not pleasant.'

'Why did you go to dance with them?'

'I liked to leave you all behind – and the tight spiked hedges you make round women – and men. I wanted to go where there's colour, and sweetness. I didn't squint very often.'

'And their faces, if you see through the illusion?'

Irritably, she said: 'You know what their faces are like. They're the dead.' She said: 'It feels empty, after those nights, you've danced all your strength away, you feel they've sucked the juice out of you.'

His heart thumped three times: his mouth dried up.

JUDITH

SHE SUCKLED goblins at her breast – those stinging bees, that black dog we knew about, but what other demons used her, and we never suspected it? It must have been so. All her babies died, one after another. Except Margaret and Bridget, and why did they survive? Because they took to the poison the spirits had made of Alice's milk. Bridget and Margaret were conceived and carried in the water of wickedness. No holy chrism could have changed them, for all their seeming pieties. They belonged to the Devil.

Margaret did well to leave the village, we'd have had to hang her, too, and before many years passed. But Parson's been strange since Alice's death. I hope he wasn't too weak to contend with her.

SIR THOMAS

THE COMMON people can be controlled by such excitements, and that is why I was content for the case to go forward to the Assizes. They vented all their bile on Alice Slade, and not on the evictions it was prudent for me to have executed. Now the trouble-makers have left. I regret none of my own actions. But Susan. I regret Susan.

I regret, in Susan, everything that made me love her, her chastity, her discretion, her sweet fidelity. I did not want her otherwise, but I do not regret the kiss she let me have.

Why did my wife Marjorie never offend Alice Slade?

ROBERT

FOR BRIDGET I wasn't the cuckolded fool of a husband, silly Robert Tarry who put his money on the wrong cock the first time he ever gambled. I stepped into Alice's house to consult about the chalice, and a young girl looked up at me, the light shining out of her grey eyes. I loved her. Bridget, who Alice kept so close, who sometimes showed her hood and skirts to the village and ran away again. I forgot all the reasons why I shouldn't marry her.

What she saw in me, I never knew, but sometimes I wondered who she was kissing.

MARGARET

MY MOTHER gave me her blessing, when I went off to live with Thomas. Glad to see me leave her house. But Bridget – that was a different matter.

Mother had always kept her in. Oh, she never forbade her to go out. Instead, she told her stories. The village her tongue built for Bridget had robbers in hiding on every path. And ghosts, as soon as the sun fell anywhere near the horizon. And when Bridget did go out, Mother would really worry herself silly all the time she was gone, and cry with relief when she came back. She'd fetched the dangers out of her head, and they grew before her eyes. She told wonderful stories, because she believed them herself.

She got Bridget to bind her breasts flat so that no one would notice she was grown up, and so want to ravish her – and cut her throat afterwards, as Mother predicted. She put a fence round Bridget stronger than any tower she could have shut her up inside. Only little by little Bridget began to understand that she was in prison. When Robert Tarry came to see Alice about the Communion cup that was missing, Bridget was already looking for the way out.

There was nothing wild about Robert Tarry, and he made his face gentle and fatherly for Bridget, his eyes were soft in his fleshy face. She must have thought the Church would shield her from Alice, and, since she couldn't marry the parson, the churchwarden would do.

Alice called Robert a thief, in which she was right, though he wasn't the kind to slit purses, still less throats. He had other ways of working. She called Bridget a whore, which was nonsense: she hadn't given Bridget the opportunity to become a whore. 'Ungrateful,' my mother screamed to Bridget, 'look what I've done for you, slattern, lazy trull!' And so on. And seized the knife and Bridget's hair – Bridget stood frozen, didn't dare resist – and hacked a few of those soft brown curls off. She'd have cut it all short if I hadn't got the knife away from her. Then it was my turn to be abused: 'Lumbering carthorse, stupid fat pig-face, worthless undutiful sack of lard!' And worse. I don't want to remember. It still hurts. But I saved the rest of Bridget's hair. She was grateful to me, but I didn't do it for her sake. I did it to thwart my mother.

CHAPTER NINE

SARAH

YOUR MEMORIES seem to turn sweet with age, like pears that only ripen when they come off the tree. You've lived so long, hoping for more, now you understand you'll get no more, so you make the best of what you've had. The sun is shining in at the window and even my eyes can see the brightness. It surrounds me, like a caress.

But the sheet's still rucked up under my leg: it hurts, and I can't smooth it – my weight – can't shift it, though I strain and grunt like the pig. The heavier the pig gets, the nearer his death. He doesn't know it. I do. And Audrey won't come if I call. And I'll wet myself waiting. It's so tedious.

Parson, visiting, tells me my reward's waiting for me in heaven. Everything I didn't have is up there for me. What? My body young again, and a man worth having between my legs? No, says Parson, his voice weary at my ignorance, there's none of that in heaven. And reads to me from the Bible. A minute later both of us notice that he managed to understand what I say, really understand for the first time.

He thought he'd master us, when he first came. With his elder brother up at the Hall, and half of us living on Sir Henry's land. Not my Martin, though. So my lads went off to fight for Parliament. If they'd been King's men, would they have lived? The same complaints, the same questions. I'm in prison here, day in, day out.

But the sunlight against my closed lids tells me tales of escape. There's a dazzly door there. Alice holds it, smiling. I never went through. The door led to death. Just once, I looked through – that was bad enough.

When Richard Berkeley first came to the parish, he was angry with all of us, but it was worst for the women. He wanted to burn Sykes's imprint off the place, mark it his own. We all knew he'd been sent away because his parents couldn't bear him, that his brother Sir Henry tolerated him, but didn't love him so much either. I don't know how anyone can make favourites among their children.

Richard Berkeley was a man with a cause. Like Sykes before him, only it had to be the opposite one. And people took badly to the endless prayers, and short sermons weren't what they were used to. When you've had a hard week's work, you'd rather doze through a long sermon than keep bobbing up and down for prayers.

I suppose Parson thought he'd subdue the men through their wives. He wanted us to feel filthy. He said we mustn't come to church if we had our time of the month, or had been with our husbands the night before. He called it God's law.

But I am filthy. I wet the bed. I gave bloody birth to lads for them to kill – but that was more blood. I don't understand these things.

Parson Berkeley had the church table shrouded like a bush on washday.

You could say we'd been spoiled. Parson Sykes had never waved the rod over us, too lost in his dreams and ideas for that, the strange little man. He never haled anyone in front of the Church courts, so most brides went to church pregnant. Richard Berkeley made Robert Tarry churchwarden (closing his eyes to Lisbeth Tarry's behaviour) and set him counting the months between every new wedding and childbed. We didn't like it.

It was the village against the parson, showing him how far he could go, and Alice was the force behind us. Alice, who once said: 'Heaven? God's a man, what good can we expect of him?' It was spring. The pale young oakleaves seemed to have been made of glass, you could smell the blossom everywhere, and the birds whistled love-songs among the white flowers of the hedges. The air was warm and full of crazy mirth.

Alice got the women together, we laughed like naughty children while we planned it. The men, when they heard about it, egged us on. For once. Usually, they're not much interested in our ideas. So we get on with our work. Alice had her own particular interest: what she was doing for a living was against the Church's laws, and it would have been bad for business if she or any of her clients had been made to do penance in a white smock. And how could she have lived, without that extra income?

She said: 'We won't go to church at all. If he takes us all to the courts, that will be more trouble for him.'

Most of us would have crumbled before it came to that. It didn't.

He sent Robert Tarry to ask us why we'd kept away from church – we blushed, and said our husbands were one and all so lusty on Saturday night (Alice's idea, when Francis Slade no longer dared come anywhere near her). We asked Robert why we had to reveal such things to a man? Did the new parson want us all shamed for ever? Robert Tarry was too red in the face himself to deal with us. When he couldn't control his own wife! He went back to Parson, I suppose, and told his master to speak to us himself.

Parson might have sent Madam Berkeley, but she was brought to bed. Luckily for us.

I mustn't smile like that. If Audrey saw me – or Parson— Oh, but the sort of dreams I still have, if Parson knew, he'd lock me out of heaven and throw the key in hell's furnace to melt away. Nothing you can do about dreams.

Our Vicar couldn't face us. Come back to church, he said. He renounced all claim to rule the kingdom between our legs. And from then on we knew what he was, a weathercock, push him and he'd spin. And, like the rest of us, he made out he believed pregnancies could last four or five months, and the child still be born plump and healthy. The first child, at least.

It changed him, to be shut up with Alice. They all say she made a good end. He's gentler, kindlier now. To himself, as well as to other people. In those days he shut himself up in his house with his wife, and gnawed at himself, and her. While Alice and I (who were each other's best friends) drank to our triumph and hugged each other. Margaret was marketing, and had taken Bridget (Alice didn't keep her quite so close, when she was a child). Francis Slade had gone drinking to town. We were alone in the house.

Vicar says I'll go to heaven if I earn it, I'll burn if I don't. He sits beside me as he sat with Alice. I couldn't confess to him.

I swear I never did anything to encourage her.

And yet the words come to me, like birds singing at nightfall. Her wondering voice: 'Sarah, you're beautiful.'

No one knows. The fruit is always sweetest when it's just about to turn rotten. That juice between my legs.

I felt no pleasure, when she kissed me on the lips. I only felt revulsion. What I feel now is a betrayal, the softness so deep in my belly, I remember that from Martin. I remember Alice's stroking hands from my childbed, from my sickness. That's it.

The feel of love in her hands!

I did not, never did, let her hands and lips move to my

breasts – 'Oh, Sarah, so small, so pink, so good to taste!'
(Martin's words), she did not suck me as a baby does, it
never ran through me, keeping me trembling, wanting
more. I pushed her away from me, I fastened my front
and ran out of the house. (Ah, but wouldn't she have
been, wasn't she, softer, more pleasant, than anyone else?)

Wasn't it quiet, there in the house?

'No one will come. My lovely one. My sweetheart.
My love. All gold, even down there, and your belly so
smooth, in spite of the children!' Her voice, really soft,
pearling: 'Your legs, so shapely and straight!' Her fingers,
so gentle, so knowing, you could melt into her. How did
she enchant me? The shame, I can't bear it – but didn't I
leave her unsatisfied, when she'd pleased me so much?

I'm glad. She had too much already. She owed me that
pleasure, and I owed her the empty longing I left her with.
She had already betrayed me.

It never happened. It is a dream.

WHEN THE bell rang four times, Satan began to smoke
like wet grass on a hot morning, at first ever so slightly,
then furiously, his substance thinning away by the minute.
And Richard, raising his eyes to the grille, saw the
morning star framed between two rusty iron bars, and
smelt the dawn wind.

He looked round the cell and understood how solid the
walls were, how slack was Alice's skin and how fragile
the thin mottled flesh that wobbled round her brittle
bones, flesh that was blue with cold and spatched with
brown, that seemed to be decaying on her already.

In spite of everything, he thought, I *am* a man of
authority.

And yet, when he said: 'Alice, I wear the cloth. You

must let me instruct you', there was still a note of pleading in his voice.

He could not hear her answer.

She said, more loudly: 'I'm tired. So are you. What should we say?'

He said: 'The words are preordained. They are written in Holy Scripture and in the law of this land. I know what you have to say.'

She said: 'The night's almost gone. Nothing can stop them hanging me in the morning.'

The water dripped out of green slime on the ceiling and fed green slime on the floor. Alice thought: The birds will be singing soon, and dawn will break. I shall come out into daylight, and see the weather again after all these months. But the humour of the sky won't matter to me after an hour. Will he say it's the day the Lord has made, and tell me to rejoice and be glad in it? She laughed, briefly. She thought: Could I ever laugh at the gallows? They'll dig me in there and some cunning woman will come for my skull, take it away and grow moss on it. She began to laugh again, heaved, grunted, guffawed with the thought.

'Alice,' said Richard. 'Alice, it appals me that you can laugh at this time.'

'Moss,' she said, tittering. 'They'll grow moss on me.'

'Alice,' said Richard, desperately: 'Alice, you will burn for ever in hell. The devils will sit you astraddle a saw and you will feel its teeth for ever slicing into you, they will hold you in a furnace that never consumes you, they will laugh, then, not you, their laughter will be hideous in your ears, you will never escape once that dreadful finger has pointed you out of His sight, after they have dragged you down into the depths of perpetual misery. Is that what you want?'

'It's nonsense,' she said.

'Woman, it has the authority of the Church.'

'And so?' she asked. 'A lie isn't any less the lie because fools have been telling it for years. The doctor the rich folks use thinks if he purges the guts out of his patients, lets half the blood from their bodies, and takes all their money, they'll mend. I wonder how many folk he's killed? And all in the name of ancient philosophy. He makes them piss in a glass, then peers into it and recommends bleeding, bleeding every time. Never mind what's in there.'

Richard sat down in his chair and put his face in his hands.

No, thought Alice. I don't want to destroy him. When I am destroyed come what may.

She said: 'I'll try to tell it the way you want. They'll hang me whatever I say, so I might as well make you happy.'

She thought: I want someone to love me.

CHAPTER TEN

JUDITH

ALICE WAS accepted in the village, when I was a child. Not only accepted, but valued. She worked, as we all did. She tended her cow, her bees, her sheep, she kept and slaughtered a pig, she skimmed the cream off, soured it; and churned it, she spun and sold wool, grew flax and made her linen. She salted pork and collected the hens' eggs in summer. She cooked, she preserved, her vegetables flourished. She dried herbs for healing and for cooking. Women's hands are always at something, hers had to be busier than most – we all know what it means for a woman to have a drunken, whoring husband. Still she was never quite one of us.

She had her place. Only my mother grumbled that Alice delivered the odd baby while her back was turned, when my mother was sick, or looking after another woman. Rightly so. My mother, after all, had her midwife's licence from the Bishop and had sworn an oath to baptise babes, in case of need, to the Church of England and nothing else. A Papist midwife would have been better than Alice, God knows what kind of baptisms Alice may have performed. I'm always wary of anyone I know she delivered. Like Martin Tidbury, the bad lot among Sarah's three sons, who has Sarah's vanity and his father's overbearing ways but none of Sarah's charm: even his good looks hit you like a blow in the face. If Alice had already baptised him to the Devil, it would make no difference how much

LESLIE WILSON

water they splashed on him afterwards. That's what I
think. But neither my mother nor the churchwardens
would have informed on Alice – you're careful how you
deal with people in a small place like this. You're especially
careful of cunning folk.

But in the end you have to draw the line somewhere.

It was Bridget's birth unsettled my mother most. Juliet
was so weak, the blood was pouring out of her, and my
mother reckoned Bridget must be dead, so she fetched the
hooks, meaning to get the babe out of her quick, so she
could die easy.

Alice hissed at her, my mother said, like a cat or a
snake, she said she wasn't having sharp iron in her sister's
body – now there's something I hadn't thought of before.
The fairies are afraid of iron – my mother says that Alice,
weak as she was from childbirth, and her own baby dead,
ran at her and pushed her towards the door. 'Look after
her yourself, then,' said my mother to Alice, 'and see how
well you get on in the state you're in.'

'I will,' said Alice.

How did Alice get away with so much, how was she
even tolerated for so long, in spite of everything?

No one knows what powers Alice used to deliver
Bridget alive and healthy. Surely Bridget should have died
like Alice's baby, bastards both and an outrage to a decent
community.

'ALICE. You are the worst of sinners. You deserve your
fate.'

'Bridget would have been killed, if I hadn't driven Ellen
out.'

'What are you talking about? You killed Bridget.'

'She'd never have lived. She was a tender tiny baby,

and Ellen Cox wanted to tear her to shreds with the hooks. I couldn't bear it.'

'You went against God's will.'

'I did what seemed right, and she came. And Juliet died gently, in my arms. She never held Bridget. Bridget was mine. I fed her on the milk that my own dead baby would never suck. She was mine. She would have died without me. And she grew up to torment me.'

'Alice, this is not the truth we need.' He thought: What is truth? The words of Pilate. I am losing everything, he thought, betraying everything.

Alice said: 'I wrapped Bridget up tight, and tied her to me, and she lay against me all the time I washed the blood off Juliet, the blood Bridget was washed in herself, and all but drowned in.' Then she saw his face. Oh, she thought, I've been saying the wrong things. It's hard to remember how to behave.

'I can't do it,' she said harshly. 'I don't know the words.'

'Alice, repeat. I have sinned. I have done the Devil's work. I deserve my fate.'

'I have sinned. I have done the Devil's work. I deserve my fate.'

SARAH

BECAUSE SHE'D saved Bridget's life at the outset, she thought she'd bought her. No, not bought her, made her, rolled her and shaped her like a wax mannikin. That was the way she was with all of us. She never gave favours, she took possession of you whenever she did anything for you. And as long as you did what she wanted, she was marvellously good to you. As long as you were exactly the person she wanted you to be. Did you transgress, she thought it was her right to destroy you. Reproaching you at the same time, look what I've done for you, I've saved your life, healed your rheumatism, delivered your baby in one piece.

Most of them only began to understand a few years back. She had to do this thing to me, before I fully understood.

Oh, she deceived us all. She had such faith in herself, her tongue was so clever to caress or to curse. She was cunning in every sense of the word. And the loving touch of her hands.

It must have been worse for Bridget than for anyone else. No wonder the poor child was so timid, no wonder the poor woman was so fearful. And Alice was forever touching her, holding her, Bridget's head on Alice's lap, Alice's hand stroking Bridget's hair, you'd have thought the two of them were one person. In spite of Robert Tarry, in spite of the church service on Sunday, prayers every morning and odd times as well, Bridget never got rid of the guilt that she'd left Alice. How should that surprise me?

MARGARET

I USED to lie in bed with Bridget like a huge sow with her piglet, far more than five years bigger and crueller than she. One day, I used to think, I'll roll over and smother her. (I shan't do it on purpose, I promised my better self.)

Sometimes her breathing would shorten, grow ragged, at last stop altogether. Her body stiffened against me, she fought her chest to stop it snatching the air against her will. Then I'd start shoving and pinching her till she cried out – then she had to breathe, but usually it would all start again within a few more breaths. If I pinched her hard enough, she'd cry herself to sleep, but that could be dangerous. My mother had good ears.

'What have you done to her? Why is she crying?' Slap. I began to cry, too, because I knew it fuddled my mother. So she'd shove something in my mouth, even when I was fourteen or fifteen.

Sometimes I asked Bridget why she held her breath.

'I don't do it,' she said. 'It happens.' I could feel her eyes turned on me, even in the dark; huge, terrified, they bored holes of deeper darkness in the room. I knew she wasn't telling the truth.

Once, she said: 'I can't say. They'd punish me.'

'They?' I knew she meant the fairies.

'Oh, they're here now, don't you see? They crowd in on me and I can't breathe, they tweak me and whisper in my ears.'

I couldn't see the slightest sign of movement, though I wanted to, God knew what they might do to me, and I'd never be able to stop them. I imagined their wicked watching eyes aglitter, they didn't care what *they* did, but they'd punish *me* for slatternliness, I knew, my mother had warned me often enough. They were her friends. I thought they had hideous angular faces, squints, and leering grins.

'You should have kept quiet,' I said. And went on, partly to torment her, partly because I was scared, too: 'You'd better not snivel, they'll be angrier still.'

I managed to fall asleep, but I'm sure she lay there all night, straining to see the first light through the cracks in the walls and shutters.

They are the dead. Did our grandfather – who was also her father – come to plague her, along with her mother –

her sister – my aunt? If so, it's a wonder my aunt could resist the temptation to give me a pinch for old times' sake.

Poor little Bridget, when my mother's loving care meant she told her endless stories – pitched so I couldn't hear more than frustrating snatches.

'He walks across that bridge now, every night, carrying his head under his arm – and in the woods on winter days, too, so you mustn't go there . . .' And: 'Margaret! Have you cooked the swill for the pig?' Or: 'And he was so desperate for money, he said the Lord's Prayer backwards three times, wrote on a paper in his own blood: "Beelzebub, here is my heart's blood, I beg five sovereigns for this reward", and put it under his pillow when he went to bed. In the night he felt the hands groping under the pillow, and lay ever so still, his blood like ice, and the paper was gone in the morning. The money appeared on the table that very day, and for a while he was happy, but then he began to hear footsteps following him, wherever he went, though he whipped round to see who it was, there was never anyone, only the footsteps – Margaret! Go and weed the flax!' And another time: 'And the cinders fell out of the fire, shaped like coffins, that's how you know someone's going to die, and the dog howled all night outside the window – that's another sign. They found him dead in the morning, his hair standing rigid from his head, his eyes round and staring, and, though no one had heard it, they could all see he had died raving.'

And Bridget would cling to my mother – oh, she was so frightened, and my mother must tell her more – and I'd look at my mother's face: she'd reached some place she'd have liked to stay, Bridget wanted her, needed her, the clutch of Bridget's desperate hands was a joy to my mother.

Then I see Bridget sitting by the polished silver bowl, and the flame of the rushlight directed into the bowl by a glass full of water. Bridget's hands were tight against her face, blocking her eyes off, and however long my mother waited, however patiently my mother talked to Bridget, coaxed her, tried to reassure her, however much fury grew and bottled up in my mother's skinny little body, Bridget would never take her hands away.

BRIDGET

YOU CALLED me your sweet, your pet lamb, I knew I was special. Only what you wanted me to do, that was the terror. I feared you might cast me out, as you did Margaret, to the horrors beyond the protection of your arms.

You loved me. You told me stories. You led me into enchanted places, some of them were terrifying, but you were there to hold onto me, so I could shiver in safety. And some of them made me laugh, you told me about ladies with faces like pigs, about bears who were humans in disguise, about the fairies putting asses' heads on foolish men.

How could I have betrayed you, except that I had no choice? Believe me. Oh, it hurt, when you began to hate me.

I can remember one short autumn day, the air was so clear you'd think it had been distilled and mellowed in the burning, there was a gentleness about the light among the red-leather beech leaves. I was a tiny child. You came from market and your hair was on fire in the sunset, the trees were bonfires of colour and the leaves flew off like sparks. I saw your face, and it was beautiful. And later they told me that you were the ugliest woman in the village.

MARGARET

IT WAS a bright windy afternoon, and the leaves ran on the ground like crowds of frightened people, then fell flat as if they were shamming dead. My mother's hair caught the evening sun – you could only see her eyes in her face, hardly even her eyes, your own swam in a dazzled blue haze. She had her hands stretched towards Bridget, but what was in her face wasn't even for Bridget – she turned aside a little. I thought she'd vanish any moment, and leave Bridget hugging empty space.

And I thought: She's lacking, dying of thirst. Now I know women in that state can't give milk to their children.

Once she took her spindle of wool, snarled several days' work up and threw it onto the fire. It stank. She stood watching it burn, and she laughed. As if she was saying: This is the way it must be. This is what my work is worth. This is what I am worth. Then a client came who had rheumatism, and she took her into the other room. Maybe the old dame thought the stench was some spell, but my mother behaved as if nothing was wrong. She never liked to admit there was anything lacking, not in those days. Not even that my father was useless.

He staggered in and out, picking invisible spiders off himself and whispering. No one took much notice of him. If he tried to get down to work, he'd damage himself, a gash in the hand when he was chopping wood, slash on the thigh from a sickle – more work for my mother.

Parson Sykes would call, and talk to my mother about the Bible – we used our church pew in those days. He'd ask her if everything she used was in accordance with the law of God. She'd smile and nod. 'Oh, yes,' she said. He'd smile back, like an idiot, which is what he was. And there was that skull growing moss in the back room. 'Look at my charms,' would say my mother, 'holy names on them, Matthew, Mark, Luke and John.' 'Good,' he would say. And glare at my father if he dared interrupt. I used to think: I'll put rotten eggs in your pocket, you carrion crow. Sykes wouldn't have noticed if I had. He'd get an exalted expression on his face, his nose would grow thin and white and twice its usual length – or so I thought – and he'd start babbling about the Kingdom of God that would come when the rest of us had been thrown on the gridiron. Which he and my mother would inherit alone, I suppose. Certainly, there'd have been no kingdom for my father.

I should have pitied my father, then. Maybe could have stopped my mother hag-riding him through the night – I'd lie in bed, listening for the jingle of the harness. She bridled him. After she'd run away from us all with a troop of thieving tumblers. She had no right to his good behaviour. She was a liar, a cheat, a disobedient whore. She came back and unmanned him. Now I wonder if I helped her. I smart at the memory of the times I showed my contempt for him, that was one of the few ways I could please her.

She was the head of the house. That's wrong. No wonder she was so pleased with Sykes's rantings, when he lost all his wits, wanted to overthrow everything and let folks do just as they pleased.

CHAPTER ELEVEN

BRIDGET

I've DECAYED, in my coffin, my face looks like any other skull. I should be asleep, no one should be able to make me know anything. But I'm helpless to move or resist: the memory grows through me like a tree-root.

It's parched summer, August, and the leaves are falling off the trees already, the roads and paths have turned to powder, the sky is hot and blue, the grass has bleached yellow and the crops are stunted, their roots pinched by the hard cracking soil. Only leathery dark weeds thrive, writhing round the barley stems. There's an itchy rash on the back of my neck that none of my mother's potions can mend.

I thought then: This is the world, it's dry and dusty and it itches. I was so sure of it that even now I expect the grass to shrivel on the grave-mound in August, I believe it happens every year, and I hear a voice in my ear – with a frightened laugh – 'Your father's walking the village at night.'

I want to escape, think I *have* escaped, but it was only my mind that ran away. I stand still and stupid. Or lie here, in my grave. It makes no difference.

———◦◦◦◦◦◦———

'SO THAT was the first time, was it, the first time you spoke with Satan?'

'Yes. Must have been.' Her eyes met his, asking: Am I

doing this well? And a gleam of unbelief – this is a game. We are conspirators.

No, he thought. I won't have it. He asked: 'And Sykes's part in this?'

He could feel her withdrawal. She said: 'In the morning, he came climbing in through the fallen yew tree – the old one, it was blown down onto the churchyard gate that night, so there's no yew there now.'

'Oh, there is, Alice. I planted one, and I will plant another. So that I have something to leave behind me, even though my son lies in his grave.'

She asked: 'What month are we in?'

'March.'

She thought: I haven't heard the birds singing this year, or found snowdrops in the winter grass. Or walked past gold hazel catkins. She shut her eyes and tried to see blackthorn twigs like gnarly claws in the morning mist, each grasping a small clear bead of water.

She said: 'I'm dead already, in here.'

'Not yet, Alice, you have a few hours left.'

Irritated, she thought: He doesn't understand. Why should I talk to him? She let her thoughts run: Ralfe Gibbons, my father, who taught me my trade, who switched me for my mistakes, who handed me over to Francis. My father's hands on the silver bowl, every scar and wrinkle showing in the rushlight. I looked, found the picture, watched the pleasure on his face every time I got it right. His black cane was by him, one short sharp cut for every mistake, no more, enough to sting and humiliate. I couldn't have borne to treat Bridget like that.

He showed me how to tease and annoy as well as how to heal – which herbs could blister, which would purge, how you gave people bad dreams. No one ever cheated my father more than once. He taught me that we had to make our clients respect us. The way was through fear.

LESLIE WILSON

He was amused by my malice, but he nipped my worst acts in the bud. He knew how to spoil my craft.

'Go too far,' he said, 'and they'll turn on you. The art is to know the boundary.' He was right.

I thought he'd have stopped me when I ran away with Daniel. I didn't know he was afraid of me, now, that he was glad to have me out of the way, because of what he was doing to Juliet, my little sister, who was too much my mother's image.

SARAH

RALFE GIBBONS went to hell, no, hell came up to his house to fetch him. Did the devils torment him, or welcome him to their company? (A cup of brimstone, Ralfe.) Whatever he did down there, three years later – though their time must be different – they sent him back up top to frighten the wits out of the villagers. He walked every night, never said a word. People used to peer out of their windows and see him pass, he looked neither to right nor to left, not Ralfe. He'd never seemed to pay much attention to anyone he met, for all he knew everything that was going on in the village. He looked through you.

Now people began to keep to their houses at night, and Widow Sharpe who had the alehouse was spitting with fury, always trouble with that family, she whined. Alice took my man before he could marry me, killed him and made a bastard of my son, now Ralfe uses his own death to put me out of business. We should have heeded her. We didn't.

Wonderfully sober the village was in those days, and honest, too, after a night-walking thief met Ralfe and went mad. He hanged himself from a tree in the forest – we

112

buried him at the crossroads with a stake in his heart so he wouldn't join Ralfe in his walking. A village of ghosts, they said, that's what we'll be. And though no one felt sorry for the Widow Sharpe, anyone felt sorry for themselves who wanted to drink a mug of ale of an evening.

I saw him once, and I wish I hadn't. He had his hair on end, white strands flying up from the cap he used to wear over his baldness. A cold light like a glow-worm: this from a man who went up like a torch at his fireside. And only once, as he walked, would he move his eyes, and that was when he passed his daughter's house where she lay beside the husband who (she boasted to me) she had cured at last of touching her. (He'd found himself, in the town, a wench whose legs were wide enough for twenty.) And no one had any doubt whose job it was to deal with the matter.

'SYKES, Alice! I want the truth about Sykes.' And he thought: Have I authority in my voice? He stiffened his neck – he *would* break her silence. 'Did he not conjure spirits with you, even before he was expelled from the Church? What was he at, the night you raised Satan in the graveyard?'

She stared at him, obstinate, mute.

'Alice, your silence will not protect him. You recognised that you must confess. Admit it. Sykes too was a witch.'

'No! He was parson then, and he said as you do, that the ghost was a devil in my father's likeness. It was a judgement on us all, he said, and a sign that the world was coming to an end. He said we should pay attention to the prophecies in the Bible. But no one took any notice of him, any more than they do of you—'

'Alice!'

'No, that's not what I meant to say. Sykes said I was to

leave him alone. My father's ghost, I mean. But I went out to him, because I wanted him to take notice of me. I had things to say to him.'

'To the Devil?'

She said: 'I remember the old yew creaking and the shadows flying across the gravestones as the moon came and went – it was a wild night. I screamed at him above the noise of the wind, you could ask the folk at the Bell, they heard me. No, I forgot, they're dead. I asked him if it was love, what he did to Juliet. I asked him what was the fire that burned him to cinders, wasn't it lust? I asked. But he was ice-cold.'

'Ice-cold?'

'Like a moving column of ice, cold as fear. You couldn't reach him.'

'Alice, he was hot, he came from hell!'

'No, he was cold.'

'He was hot. His breath scorched you. He had cloven hoofs. He leered.'

'No, his face was set. It didn't move.'

'He leered at you, Alice, and breathed on you with his hot and lustful breath, he taunted you—'

'He never spoke a word.'

'Alice, hell gapes!' He thought: I will force her to tell it as I want it. I must. Or *I* will die.

She thought: What difference does it make now? They will believe what they want to believe.

'Sir, he was hot. He leered at me. He taunted me. And he said he'd give me power.'

'Now, Alice, the truth is out!'

'I said he'd have been better to give me good looks than power. He never answered.'

'No, Alice, he said, "With power you can do what you want to anyone who offends you." Didn't he?'

'Yes, sir.'

'And then?'

'Sir, I said – and now I know it's true – ' I am losing my way again, she thought, the truth is not what he wants from me. Still she continued: 'I said the power didn't amount to much, a little tinkering here and there, but the big things, the harvests, and what great folk do with us, all we could do was take the edge off it, we gave ourselves a place that way. They came to us for remedies and small spells, they brought us their petty hopes and fears and the things they had lost and their hatreds. And I cried, because we can never really change anything.' She complained: 'I did want to hurt people, but it wasn't the way you're making me tell it.'

'Alice,' he said earnestly. 'Do not cry now. Rejoice in it, Alice. That God is strong enough to defeat all your evil ends, aye, and bring you to salvation at last.' He felt a power greater than himself washing all his imperfections away, bearing him up on a royal scarlet torrent. 'Yet – how can you say you could change so little when you could kill? Wait, don't answer. That was it, wasn't it? When he gave you the power to kill? No, you had already killed. Your husband's half-brother, the father of Simon Sharpe.'

Her body was heavy as lead. She thought: It's so late to be awake, the rope's going to snap with the weight of my weariness. He wants me to speak. What did he say?

'He reminded you – didn't he? – that he had given you this power, and that you could kill again? Didn't he? Didn't he?'

'Yes. Yes.' Have I said enough? she thought. I don't like to be driven.

'And what happened then?'

'Sir, I felt sorry for him.'

'Sorry for Satan! Go on.'

She thought: I'm too tired to guess what he wants.

She said: 'I told him it was time to sleep. I said, sleep, Father, rest. Rest, Father, sleep. The wind blew a tile off the church roof and it flew straight through him and buried itself in the turf. And every time I spoke he sank a little further down, first his knees, then his waist, then his chest. I was so tired, but I kept saying the words. He never told me I could rest. I was so tired. So tired—'

'Wake up, Alice! They were the wrong words. Say now: "Get thee behind me, Satan." Say it, Alice!'

'Get thee behind me, Satan.'

'Now tell me more.'

'I remember his hair, it was the only part of him still above ground, it was standing up out of the grave-mound like white grass in the frost, while the green grass flattened under the wind—'

'Alice. He pulled you down and thrust his stinking fiery member into you, and you did revel in that degradation, and when he left off, Sykes the Ranter, the renegade, the man of Belial, came in and took over. Did he not? And did he not, even in these last years, provoke you to shameful and unnatural lust, did he not instruct you that all things come by nature? That there is no God but inside your own head? Did you not enjoy each other, contrary to the law of God and your own ancient and repulsive state? Did you not slake your devilish lusts on his member that should long since have been quiescent, and how else could that have happened but with the connivance of Satan?'

I cannot forgive Sykes, he thought. They put him in the family parish when I was a boy intended for the priesthood, they promised him a long tenure, so they could send me away to the other end of the kingdom. He sat on my property for a while, then threw it away, as if he despised it. He was a traitor, so many times a traitor there should be no punishment vile enough for him, yet he walks free, while I sit in this stinking cell with a stubborn and evil old woman. She shall obey me.

'No, sir. No.'

Something flew twittering past him, brushing his head with leathery bat-wings. He looked up in horror, and saw a fiend with Susan's features. He put his hands to his face to protect it, but the creature was too quick for him. It landed on his lips, kissed them, and veered away.

RICHARD

SHE WAS stubborn, to protect Sykes. Did I press her too hard on this subject, she would pretend to be wandering, so that no sense came out. I was angry. I thought if I had him there I could have brought him to confess, as I brought her. But now I think witches cannot lie for ever, and Alice was beginning to learn the truth. So it may be that she was right, that Sykes is indeed innocent on this count, though guilty of sedition, indecency, and concupiscence. And crazy to boot.

'SYKES, Alice, I want to know about Sykes!'

'I'm cold. I'm tired. I'm hungry. What did you say? I can't hear.'

'Tell me what you practised with Sykes!'

'Poor silly child. That's what he said.'

'Alice!'

'I was lying worn out in the churchyard grass, he could see my red hair, so he thought I was a fox asleep. The little foxes, you know, that spoil the vineyard. And our vines have tender grapes. Your hands must be tender to pluck them. Let him kiss me with the kisses of his mouth, for his love is sweeter than wine—'

Richard listened to her. I cannot tell her this is indecency, he thought, and his hands felt the weight of his befuddled head. This is Holy Scripture.

Again, he saw Susan's face, but disembodied this time, smiling anxiously against the rough stones of the cell wall.

CHAPTER TWELVE

'YOU HAVE been unchaste, have you not?'

'Yes.'

'And do you now most bitterly repent?'

'Yes. I have to repent it.'

He thought: She does not mean a shred of this, I should challenge her, I should get down to a proper level of truthfulness, should drive God's message into the pit of her soul. Then he thought: But there is no time. I must take what she gives me, and pretend I believe it.

She thought: The hands, Daniel's, James's – the memories swim together in my head, the dreams come out to tug me away from wakefulness. Richard Berkeley doesn't want to let me go.

He wants to steal my rest after I'm dead; he says they'll go on questioning me over there. But James told me heaven and hell are only lies invented to frighten poor people, we go back to Mother Earth, that's what I want to do, I want to sleep in her arms. James said priests and ministers know they're lies, all the time they stand there telling them in the pulpit. The powers that be, said James, make themselves a God. He says God is within us.

We made heaven right there in my bed.

James's hands were old, shaky, shiny, cracked, thick-veined, but quick to learn skill with my body, and gentle. While Daniel's – Daniel's were young (at the other end of my life), long-fingered and light-fingered, smooth as a lazy lord's – and my lord liked to be lazy whenever he had the chance, 'Let me sleep, Alice,' he'd say, 'if you'd lived your life on the road as I have, you'd like a bed when you'd got it, what's wrong with you that you have to be so busy?' I could laugh to think how hard it was for me to learn idleness and sleep. I could take to them easily now.

If there was food to eat, and ale – or better still, wine – to drink, Daniel didn't care that there might not be enough of either the next day. His hands were slim as a woman's, and gentle as the slide of a snake across the earth. He'd throttled a man with them once. So said Oliver, the ginger-haired bearkeeper, who warned me not to offend Daniel in case he strangled me too. Oliver hated me. He was in love with Daniel himself, and so was the strong man, Jonas – only Daniel went with Jonas from time to time, never with Oliver, who had to spill his lust inside his bear.

Richard Berkeley knows nothing of what happened in London. I never told anyone about it. It stayed mine, that way.

It was the time of year that people left the village. After the Goose-quill Fair on August tenth, outside the Bell. People were very restless, that year. The harvest had failed again, stomachs would shrink that winter, and it was time to clear the reckoning, cut your losses, abandon your land, or your master.

Or your husband and baby daughter. No, she was five years old, no baby, but a great pig's bladder of a child. And I never loved her, and she hated me from the moment she was born. I knew she wouldn't miss me. And if Sarah missed me, Sarah who I loved so cruelly—

SARAH

HER EYES never left him, not even to watch the bear tear a gash in Peter Gough's cheek, when Peter tried to prove his manhood by boxing with him. And serve him right for a dirty thief and bully, said the rest of us. Hadn't Peter Gough been bound over to keep the peace after he threatened my father-in-law with a red-hot iron? Hadn't Alice taunted him with his pilfering, and wasn't he probably the thief who had turned coward and dumped the chalice in a ditch? And foul-mouthed with it. He was a clever smith, but no one was sorry the night he got too drunk and tumbled face-first into the village pond. I shut my eyes now – there is Peter at the fair, reeling away from the mangy beast's claws, and the bear looking at its paw as if it were wondering what it had done, and why Peter was shouting abuse at it. And everyone laughing, and my eyes go to find Alice's, to share the joke – but the smile on her face is for the tumbler.

Oh, the rest of us were delighted for a while, till we noticed the patches and holes in the bright clothes, the untrustworthiness of his pretty mouth, the battered state of his flying baubles when they lay still beside him and he was tipping ale down his throat. But Alice was caught. She had lost all hold over herself. She stepped away from me, into that illusion.

ALICE SAT on the filthy cell floor, and thought: I could imagine those hands on my body, when he turned his slanted green eyes on me.

Her tongue repeated the confession Richard was teaching her, she thought: I don't have to stay with my body any more. How clever of me!

★

THE BAUBLES flew so fast they lost their colour, the tumbler's body curved like a squirrel's, he bent into the air and bounced from his hands to his heels, he stood upright and smiled. There was gaiety all through him. His eyes were painted. He swallowed fire and picked money out of the villagers' clothes as if he was finding lice.

She had never been moved by a man's body before. He smiled at her, taking possession of her.

So she left Francis lying in his vomit on the cottage floor. The first night, in the inn, Daniel ran his hand over the marks of her husband's violence and whistled gently. He said nothing. She fired up to his touch, sweet as honey.

She felt the Good Folk all around her, who make nothing of marriage bonds. They looked on shamelessly, nodded, and laughed at her pleasure.

SARAH

HE WAS the Devil, maybe. She went away with him and learned the craft she used to kill me. Or rather, to half kill me – she must be laughing, wherever she is now?

What had I done to her then, to make her take off and leave me here? I wish I could have run away with her myself: we could have dressed as men and taken to the road.

But I was a wife with three sons. She was a wife with one daughter, though it made no difference to her. And my husband, though a stolid lump, was good to me.

All that year I had to listen to them whispering and guessing in the village, let them imagine Alice with that cheat, that unnatural creature who was more than half a woman. It rained more than ever before and my pattens used to get stuck in the mud.

THE DAYS fell off that year like leaves from a tree. At first Alice told herself there would be no emptiness waiting at the other end.

She told fortunes, half of them were lies as bright as spinning balls. That made no difference – they were on the move. Now and again they would spend a day in one place, lounging, in bed as much as possible. She learned his body, while the rain patted the window panes. His shoulders, the shape of his back, his slim hard arms, his member that lay soft in her hand and then quickened to its work, his legs and his small hard buttocks. His face was smooth under her lips: he had very little beard. Then sometimes she was almost outraged that she could feel so much wanton satisfaction, and her body numbed itself, refused to feel its pleasure.

These were the times he often left her for Jonas, the strong man. Then she would cry, and the pain brought her back to reality. Daniel would let her burn for him before he came back: she hated him for it, but she was delivered up to him, she wanted it that way, even the hate. There was a brightness over each day, even in rain, even in squalor.

Whatever her hands were at, they were always wanting to touch Daniel. She hated Oliver, with his ginger hair and lascivious eyes. She understood him too well. She was outraged that he nursed the same desire she felt, that he wanted to touch Daniel who was hers. He has his bear, she said to herself. Let him make do with the beast.

The bear would crouch, next to Oliver, a little mangy, but good-natured if not sorely provoked, its chain tumbling in the dust, its near-set eyes always a little puzzled, as if it were trying to fathom the humans who surrounded it. It liked sweet cakes, and drowsed after it had been given ale to drink. Alice found herself wondering if its pelt were a coat it had chosen to wear. What sort of body would be laid bare if it undressed, would it be a bright and wonderful boy, perhaps, too pretty for Oliver?

It might have turned into something like the pig-faced lady who travelled with them for two months. She had a lovely body, and ate out of a silver trough, looked meekly about her with tiny white-lashed eyes above her snout, and adjusted her red silk petticoat with a dainty hand. While the pungent harsh stink of pig ran straight up your nose. The pig-faced lady drew crowds: for them the smell was part of the attraction.

After they had wondered at her, they came to Alice to have their fortune told. She looked into her silver bowl and talked about riches, lovers, fine fat children, while sometimes a noose formed on the surface of the bright metal, or a human armpit grossly swollen with plague. Once, while she was telling a fortune, she saw in her bowl the last client, who had left her five minutes ago with his step light and his thoughts full of the bag of gold she had promised him, fall silently to the ground with a knife in his back and rage on his face. She turned her eyes away quickly then, for fear he might see her looking on. She watched Daniel swallowing fire, and three of the audience who were sneaking round behind him to see if the flames were coming out of his rear.

The pig-faced lady vanished one night, which was bad for everyone else's trade. Her keeper was furious. Daniel laughed.

'He's paid the price for his squeamishness,' he said. 'If he'd shared a bed with her, she wouldn't have been able to flit.'

'She's been kidnapped,' said Alice, 'and shut in a sty, and the farmer's wife will wear her red silk petticoat.'

'Turned back into a human being, more likely,' said Daniel, 'tired of her stinking job, and glad to be a maidservant, or a whore.'

Alice said: 'Ah, but she'll snore at night.'

Alice kept her face sly that year, but she was as entranced as any other country bumpkin. Daniel knew, and he laughed at her: he said she would learn better.

One night they had to sleep huddled together in the snow. Alice slept back to back with the bear, and its rough hair scratched her. Towards the end of the year, she knew she was going to have another child. She never expected it to live.

SARAH

I WENT to the church porch on Midsummer's Night that year. The only time I've ever done it, and I was the only watcher. Strange how you never remember who told you these things: I only knew, as if I'd been born with the knowledge, that if you stay there at midnight you see next year's dead walking towards you.

I waited, and whispered: 'Alice. Alice.'

There was a mist, and my hair curled out of my hood. I could just see the churchyard gate, a wooden roof over pillars of flint. I was so cold. I thought how young I was still, thought about my body, so smooth and pretty inside what I'd thrown round me to keep the cold off: a jewel, I thought, rough-wrapped.

Did I want to see Alice's wraith, or the woman herself, returned to the village? I don't know.

The mist grew thicker, you couldn't see the gate any

more. Suddenly I thought a hand would come from behind and tap me on the shoulder – I wanted to run away, then, but not into the mist with all the tombstones hiding in it, nor into the unlit church that was full of shadows. Some beast ran out of the night and back into it – maybe Alice did come, but in a different body, so I never guessed.

I screamed when I saw them, but the sound was cut off by the mist. It separated like curdling milk, and there they were, only faintly coloured, but you knew them. There were a few old people, a pregnant woman, and then Juliet, moving smooth as she always did, following on the heels of her father Ralfe. They walked up to within a foot of me, their eyes on the ground, then they plunged down as if they were being sucked over the edge of an invisible waterfall. Their feet never touched the church porch.

I'd have gone mad if I'd met their eyes. I know that.

Then I was alone in the mist again, and Alice hadn't come. I cried bitterly. I forgot to be afraid, and ran home, though I could only see two feet away from me. I lifted the latch and thought of Martin, lying in there waiting for me, ready to stir and put his arms out for me. I fled away from my own home. I went to Ralfe's cottage.

He came to the door, when I knocked. Did he know I'd seen him at the church porch? It's hard to believe he didn't. He stared at me, his dark old eyes were malicious and knowing. I was afraid, and when he asked what I wanted, I said: 'Nothing. Nothing.'

I said, 'Nothing.'

THEY WERE making less money, either because they had lost the pig-faced lady, or because the year was a bad one. So they found their way to London. Daniel said there was always money in London. The city was carelessly savage:

beggar's corpses lay in the streets like mice thrown down by a well-fed cat. The dark was alive with fear. One night Alice was walking alone with a fat chicken she had stolen – it was easy to steal, in the namelessness of the city – and was ambushed by two men in a dark alley. There was murder in their eyes, and worse. There was no time to be afraid: a raw strong fury took her. She wrenched the clutching hands from her throat, swung round, and glared straight at first one, then the other. I'll sear their eyes, she thought. They yelped, turned, and ran away, their hands over their faces. She smiled, and went home with the chicken.

She delivered a baby and throttled it, in an itching, stinking inn. The mother was hungry and desperate, not only because the birth was hurting so much. She asked Alice: 'It'll die, won't it?'

Alice knew what she wanted. No one had ever asked her to do this before, but she said: 'Yes. It will be born dead.'

Death, however, had his own ideas: he wanted to spare the child and take the mother. Alice wheedled him and struggled with him, to win the mother's life. She smiled to see the cord round the baby's neck as it came out: it would have been easy to slip it over the small head, but she pulled the pulsing blue thing tight and blotted out the marks of her fingers.

'Dead,' she reassured the mother. 'Never gave a cry.'

The mother sighed with relief.

That night she put her hand palm to palm with Daniel's, and thought: Throttlers, both of us. He smiled and made love, so gentle, so tender, she thought she was on her way to heaven.

She went too far.

Not by hating Oliver: Daniel hated him too, and Oliver's desire for Daniel was laced with loathing. Once

they pulled knives on each other, but Daniel subdued
Oliver, then drew back from the kill, and they made a
joke of it.

ALOUD, she said: 'It would have been all right if I'd
poisoned him.'

'What?' asked Richard. He thought: She isn't with me,
everything is going horribly awry, and she will make a
fool of me on the scaffold, and I am a fool, I am
incapable—

'If I wanted to stay with Daniel,' she said earnestly to
Richard, 'I shouldn't have made Oliver crawl up the wall
of the inn and all the way across the ceiling. Like a fly,
and there were so many people watching. I shouldn't have
shown myself so powerful. I lost him,' she whimpered. 'I
lost Daniel.'

Richard's bafflement dissolved in pity and pain. He
thought: Yes, we lose them. That is what happens.

OLIVER TAUNTED her, picking and etching at the miracle
of Daniel's desire for her. He said it would have been less
perverse of Daniel to have bedded the pig-faced lady, he
told Alice how ugly she was, lingering over every detail.

Then one day Alice found herself asking Daniel if he
loved her. He laughed, and she knew the end had come.

SHE SAID to Richard: 'I get angry, I turn cold, it goes into
my tongue, and poison drips out, that's why you've got
me here, why you're going to have me throttled with a
rope.' Malice crept into her face. 'I was pleased to do it,'
she said. 'I was proud of myself. It wasn't my fault that
they didn't appreciate it. Wouldn't you think people

who'll pay to see a woman with a pig's face would pay more to see a ginger-haired bear-leading pervert crawling upside down across a painted inn ceiling, begging me not to let him drop, and his blubbering tears falling into the mouths of the fools gaping underneath?'

'Alice,' he asked, 'what are you telling me?'

She said: 'I stole all Daniel's money the night I left him, and he lay with his eyes shut – oh, he knew what I was doing, but he probably thought a bag of gold wouldn't have been too much, if it would get rid of me. I saw it in his face when Oliver reeled off to vomit his humiliation on the dung-heap.'

She began to laugh. Richard found his bewilderment and fear shiver and change inside him, I am falling, he thought, and he was laughing with Alice. The cell was full of little winged forms, the batwings of devils brushing with the pigeon-feathered plumes of small giggling cherubs, all chasing, tumbling, playing in the air. Then they were gone.

'Alice,' said Richard, recalling himself (I am going mad, he thought), 'it is getting late.'

MARGARET

RAIN AND MUD, and the road slithers under your feet, you stumble over the huge soft ruts. I'm not as young as I was. I'm beginning to feel tired. I wish it wasn't raining. Did my mother walk this way with her company of cheats and thieves?

The people we meet talk about thieves, highway robbers, trying to frighten country bumpkins on the move who are good for a laugh. The rain lies like a shroud on the high hedges.

My father turned robber, they say. He did no work, all the year my mother was gone, but he always had money in his pockets. Where did he get it from? they asked. I was at my grandfather's, under the care of my aunt Juliet. Bridget's mother. He took me there the first night after my mother had disappeared. He whipped me first. He'd spent all day looking for her, and hadn't found her.

It was war from the first between Juliet and me. Not that we quarrelled, we hardly ever spoke. But I hated her for being there when my mother wasn't. While she locked the food away from me, because I was so greedy.

They say now Juliet was dumb: that's a lie. She had a voice, and once a week or so she used it. She was stranger even than my mother, a beautiful statue of chalk, so pale she was greenish, and her hair bright, and her eyes dark blue. You never heard her moving round the house, she went too smooth, as if she was on wheels. Her shoulders shifted a little and her arms swayed like water weeds in the current. She didn't want me there: I was a disturbance.

There was money in the house that was never used. The coins sat in rotting bags upstairs, I would go up and play with them, heaping them up, rolling them, carefully feeding each coin back in through the ragged mouse-gnawed holes. I spun them, and they made shining worlds in the half-dark – no glass windows in those walls, though my grandfather could have afforded to put them in. The house had a silence that muffled everything.

The light had to sneak in through the chinks in the wall: cobwebs years deep made grey velvet of the rafters, and I sat upstairs playing with unspent money while God knows what was happening down below.

I felt no pain. Felt nothing, that was what that house did to you. Feeling went out of it when my mother left to get wed. Even now the memory drugs me, and the bite of the rain, the ache of my legs, all fade away into an endless suffocating patience.

But whispers echo in the dull grey attic: 'Great belly,' they said. 'Juliet's getting a great belly. And who', they demanded, 'is the father?' Answering voices: 'No sense in trying the church courts, with Parson Sykes so lax, so wrapped up in his books and his thoughts. Let them go their own way, they're different from us, and Ralfe, who wants to cross him?'

They were all so afraid of Ralfe, my grandfather. And of Juliet, who I hardly ever believed was a real woman.

The sun leaps out of the clouds, a burst of red fire low in the sky. I can't look, I mustn't see. But even if I close my eyes I can see exactly what happened. I was the one who told the village. After my aunt had been so careful to say my grandfather set himself alight when he moved too close to the fire.

There was no fire. The grate was cold. He was sitting in front of it, sure enough. Exactly as I'd always known him. Aunt Juliet was spinning, my grandfather was frowning, the creases on his forehead looked as if they'd been hacked out, and his face was grey as the spent fire. His grey eyes moved to my aunt, but hers, which knew he was looking for them, sheltered under their lids. And suddenly, I thought: She is real. She's hurting inside.

Then my grandfather's ash-grey face began to glow a smouldering red, bright flames spat out of the creases on his forehead, yellow, blue, orange-colour, green even, spread to his hair – it flew up like a burning bush – travelled down his arms, his clothing. Even his shoes took fire. Juliet grabbed me, and even at that moment I thought how strange it was that her hands were hard and strong, not languid, and she was clumsy for once as she pulled me out of the house. She was shaking with a ragged violent shaking that spread to me: it was as if we were one person. We stood outside and watched and shook.

The old wood was eager to take fire, and it burst out along the beams of the house, swallowing the rubble and daub in between. The cat streaked out with her tail alight and vanished, but the spiders must have shrivelled in the flames and the mice must have roasted alive. I thought the cobwebs would go so quickly they wouldn't have time to burn. Then the neighbours began to arrive with their little buckets of water that never did any good. Chattering and exclaiming over the biggest thing that had ever happened in that village.

Nothing was left, not the coins, nor a trace of even the largest bone in my grandfather's body, but at Parson Sykes's command, and against his own will, Sexton Hargrave scooped a coffin-full of ashes from the place where the hearth had been, and they buried that in the churchyard.

The last flames were still dancing on the ruins, and it began to rain, steady soft lines of rain that sizzled and danced on the embers, and a wet-faced figure with sodden hair came walking through the rain as if she had brought it with her. It was my mother. Nothing seemed to surprise her, neither the ruins, nor the crowd of gabbling excited villagers, nor my aunt's great belly. And her own was as swollen.

'I came back for you,' she said to me. 'Only for you.'

A miracle I didn't choke, when she shoved that down my throat. But I swallow everything I'm given. I'm big Margaret, forever chewing.

CHAPTER THIRTEEN

JAMES SYKES

IT WAS always, for as long as I can remember it, a village of sudden silences. Its inhabitants would break off in the middle of their talk, stare helplessly at one another, and shut up their minds with some worn-out proverb: 'All's well that ends well', it might be. And walk away with their fear intact inside them. They knew the catch in the throat, the tightness of the slowly throttling heart. Their breath did not come easy. There was fire, there was plague, there was robbery and violent death. For comfort, they tormented themselves with tales of witchcraft, and blamed their troubles on others. Yet who am I to condemn them, who was just as reluctant to take my life in my hand like a candle, and let it brave the wind?

How many mornings did I not see the sky red, and think it was Judgement Dawn! When it was only the bad rising of another sullen day. I thought I loved them, but I despaired of them. I was sick of them all. I fell asleep praying that the Apocalypse would rid me of them, yet go out of bed with knees weakened when I wondered what account I would give him (who I then deemed my Lord) of the flock I laid claim to. I took as my text: 'Their roots shall be as rottenness, and their blossom shall go up as dust.' Has it not come to pass, was it not always so? But other lines from the Prophet were meant for me as well: 'Hear ye indeed, but understand not, see ye indeed, but perceive not.' Fat hearts in all our breasts, our ears heavy, our eyes tight shut!

And now they say their eyes are opened, they hear what they turned away from before. But their hearts, which should direct sight and hearing, are steeped in poison. Dead. Their thoughts are of death and killing. They slit the throats of pigs, and knock rabbits over the head when they break from the last square of uncut corn. Yet sit shivering lest their own precious bodies might suffer. They go picking through their memories, out of which they pluck the lice of their malice, look, they say, this proves Alice was wicked, that she was a killer, always, how we were deceived! Lice prove the bearer's filth, no more. Oh, how hard it is to see others wallow in the mire I have escaped!

For I once wanted Alice and her father Ralfe, my rivals, in the flames of hell – I would warm my hands at their punishment, and a voice would tell me: 'Well done.' Now I will not let myself slip back into a poisoned mind. I will push away the false image I made of Alice, and what do I see instead? A young wife with a worthless husband, who held her head up with an effort. Whose eyes were too large in her white face. She had strength, and much wisdom – which came of nature. The villagers were not wise, so they feared her. They used her services, gawped, wondered, and gossiped.

When Francis sowed his child in her, her belly hung heavy, you would have thought it was too heavy for her to carry.

JUDITH

SHE WAS a killer, she was the death of her brother, she stole her mother's eaglestone that should have kept her safe in childbirth, and Lydia died, bringing Juliet into the world. Alice must have clawed her way out of Lydia's womb like a baby cockatrice. And she was an unnatural mother. She pushed Margaret away from her, when my mother delivered the baby. 'It's like him,' she said. 'Why didn't it die? I won't bear any more lumps for him.' My mother slapped her: she was at the end of all patience, weary with the long-drawn-out labour, and the bad harvest meaning we were all hungry, and lying awake at night worrying about the rent, and how to get hold of a little more money – and Alice complaining, who earned enough to get by.

Alice tried to kill her husband. She should have succeeded. Francis would have been no great loss, and Alice would have burned for petty treason, as she was not allowed to burn as a witch.

My grandmother delivered Alice and Juliet. She baptised them both as soon as she saw them, hoping they'd lose that uncanny look in their eyes. They were Ralfe's children, and they didn't. But now I see the shadow of that look in all our faces.

Ralfe once fetched a thief all the way from Dublin with the bag of silver he'd stolen. The thief had to hand the money back to its owner, then Ralfe waved his black stick three times, the wind blew, and the thief was gone. Back to Dublin, said Ralfe, who got his cut of the silver. The client felt no fear at all while he was in the house with Ralfe, but the moment he left, his hair jumped on end and stayed that way all the six miles home. People travelled twice and three times that distance to consult Ralfe, and, later on, to ask Alice's advice. It was their village: that's what outsiders thought.

When I shut my eyes, I see her on the floor of her house. Her hair has come loose and is full of blood and dirt. She stares at me with a yellow look, like a snake's.

Blank and dangerous. Then I open my eyes and see a thin black scurrying in the corner. I won't go mad, will I?

She haunts me at night. I can't get free of the memory. In my dreams, she says: 'I'll tell your mother's secret. It will disgrace all of you.'

I only see the scurrying out of the corner of my eye. It's not real. It isn't.

I'll go and put another stone on her grave. At noontime, when the sun is brightest.

They all knew too much, everyone knows that. Except Jacob, Alice's brother – my mother said he was an idiot. Maybe Ralfe took the brains out of his skull and fed them to Alice for pap.

Margaret is alive, and she knows our secret. I'm sure she knows. But she's gone. Did Alice tell the Parson? Did she?

SARAH

IT WAS six months before Francis had Alice's maidenhead – he went half mad with desire. It served him right. Before the wedding he staggered drunk about the village, boasting: he was going to wed the ugliest woman in the kingdom, and if that wasn't worth getting drunk about – he'd drink himself blind, he said, on his wedding night. And he'd beat her, he said. A woman, a dog, and a walnut tree—

It served him right for wanting her. And Alice was a stronger woman than ever he was a man. She fed him so many potions to cure his lust that she all but sent him to the next world. He was useless, all those six months. And I was glad, and I still am glad. In spite of everything.

★

ALICE SAID: 'What is it I am supposed to have done?'

Richard said: 'Alice, that is what you have to tell me.'

She said: 'I can tell you who stole your chalice, the one I found.' She smiled at him, almost flirtatiously. He clenched his hand. If I slap her, he thought, she will get the upper hand again.

'Alice, your crimes are the issue, not those of others.' And he thought: Outer deeds alone cannot purify a man. It is the complete inward posture of the soul. And so we are both lost.

'Lost,' he said aloud.

'Lost what?' she asked, thinking: What does he want of me now?

He said: 'Nothing either of us can find.'

And she thought: James Sykes, your old hands will never stroke me again. While his mind's eye saw an orchard of apples, children running between the grey-green trunks, himself among the unripe fruit and the stiff round leaves, perched in the fork of two branches. He had got up without help. But he couldn't get down again. He had to wait for someone to find him.

'Death,' he said. 'You abandoned yourself to Satan, and spread death and destruction. We are digging for the roots now, Alice. I want to know when it began. Your husband, for example, did you try to kill him?'

'If I did,' said Alice, 'I was clumsy at it, wasn't I? No, I didn't. Leave me alone.'

But she thought: When I blew him out with fly agaric, when he thought he was going mad, when I blistered his back with crowsfoot, dried up his seed and his urine with extract of cypress cones; when I made him piss the bed with dandelion, and fed him Venus's enemy, amaranthus, what did I want? Everything short of his death: I didn't want to be burned. And when I knew he was going near his whores, when I'd fed him wild clary before he set out:

it made him mad with lust and he staggered home and lay on the bed like a white corpse. I'd look at his limp member and wish it would never rise again. Then one night, when he spent himself in his sleep, I snipped the stain out of the linen, knotted it hard, and threw it into the dry well. He was knotted inside, he could do nothing to any woman, wasn't that a kind of killing?

'No,' she said aloud. 'I didn't. But I was afraid of knives, because of what I might do to him. Or to myself.'

He said: 'Yes?'

No, thought Alice, I won't tell you how I wanted to cut away the part of myself that throbbed when Sarah put her arm round me, if you knew what the smell of her did to me, the soft movement of her breathing body! My body answered if she brushed against me, my hands longed for her – I could give her pleasure, I thought, her clumsy great husband could never do what I could – she'd groan with pleasure at my caresses. You'll never know all that, Richard Berkeley. There are some things even a witch doesn't dare confess.

I could have put a cold knife blade to my wrist and drained all that bad blood. I didn't, because I wanted the desire. So I was afraid of knives. Sarah. Women may not have such loves, and I've always known it, but she's been the strongest love of my life, and scoured my heart as no man has ever done. Women's knowledge of each other makes them the crueller. Oh, she's enticed me and used me! And betrayed me.

SARAH

SHE'S BETRAYED me, she was witching me from the first time we played together as children. So clever, sometimes, at covering up her malice! Which has laid me down here, wet and cold, longing for death. A few meagre scraps of sunshine come through the window and warm the floor, to taunt me.

She was so gentle, when I was brought to bed the first time! Everyone else who could have helped me was laid low with fever. I sent Martin for Alice: she had seen enough childbeds to know what she was doing. And it was an easy birth. I was always fortunate that way. They used to say I was a child of good fortune – till my sons died. Did she arrange that?

She delivered me with skill, cared for me tenderly, stayed the fortnight to look after me and the baby. She wiped me clean and kept me warm. They think you're worth such attentions, when you're young.

No quarrels in that fortnight, no fierceness.

She smiled at my eldest son and perverted him. Or he wouldn't neglect me so now. I never loved him the way I loved the others.

Didn't I repay her attentions, didn't I help care for her when Margaret was born? And stopped Ellen Cox smacking her face, when she said she didn't want Margaret?

SARAH BETRAYED me, thought Alice. She led me on, she played at pains she never had, all to get my hands on her, she softened me, my body melted for love. And when I came home, Francis wanted me. The linen must have rotted away in the dry well. I gave way. I thought it might scratch the itch for me. But he thrust his hard member into my itch, drew blood, and hurt me.

'Yes,' she said aloud. 'I wanted to destroy Sarah, I wanted to shame her, to rob her of her beauty.'

Richard jumped in the chair where he had been dozing, and demanded: 'What was that?'

'I knew you all too well,' said Alice. 'You had so many secrets that were no secrets, you lived in fear. You grew a burden to me. So I burdened you. You owed it to me. But you didn't want to pay, you've never wanted to pay. Thieves and fraudsters, all of you.'

She felt malice and hatred strengthen within her; her hands clawed and itched for a throat to throttle. A fatter one than the baby's little neck in the inn. Margaret's, maybe. I have killed, she thought, it is true. I want to kill again. Above all, I want to kill this treacherous softness, tenderness, pity. None of it does me any good.

'You're cruel,' she complained aloud, and the strength seeped out of her. 'Cruel to a harmless old woman.'

MARGARET

I HAVE a dreadful nightmare, some nights – I don't know where it comes from. Nothing else is like it. I wake up, sleep again, and there it is once more. I struggle against it. I'm alone with it. It's as if I was being suffocated, in the dark a greater dark presses down on me, squeezing me, everything inside me screams for help, I'm going down, down, into darkness. I think I'm going to die. It lets up, I'm free of it, I seem to wake, and it comes again. What is it that attacks me, those nights?

SARAH

ALICE WAS so narrow, and Margaret such a large baby, it took days to bring her to birth. We thought Alice would die. She fell into exhausted sleep between the pains, then her drained face would look at us, pleading: Oh, will it never let me go?

However many births you've been to, your own first time is a shock, even if it's easy. I tried to be good to Alice – thinking, maybe, if I gave her back her kindness, she wouldn't want any more of me. I wiped her face and stroked her belly every time it steeled itself to fight its burden. And Ellen Cox soured with pleasure at Alice's suffering, and complained of the endless time she was taking.

'Alice,' I said. 'I'm with you.'

'Stop talking nonsense,' said Ellen Cox, who was as self-righteous and blunt-tongued as her daughter Judith. 'We'll have to get the hooks to her. She's too idle to get this babe out.'

Alice opened her eyes and hatred looked out of them.

'No,' she said.

'She'll burst,' said Ellen across Alice's body to me.

'I won't,' said Alice. 'Don't let her get the hooks, Sarah. I won't let his brat kill me.'

Right from the start, Margaret was her enemy.

Ellen Cox was shocked. She said Alice should have had some thought for her baby, even if it was needful to kill it. Ellen was still angry with Alice for delivering me of Martin, though who else could have done it, things being as they were – Ellen said it wasn't right for a woman who'd never borne a child. But Ellen thought she owned every big belly in the village.

Then Alice screamed: 'Get it out of me!' At the same moment her face crumpled, her body heaved, and the baby came in a rush with her head all out of shape. Margaret tore her mother badly, but Alice mended. She knew what to use to heal herself, better than Ellen ever knew. That was another reason Ellen didn't like her.

I wrapped the messy red creature in a clean piece of

linen and put it in front of Alice's face: she had her eyes tight shut.

'Alice,' I said. 'Here's your baby.'

Alice opened her eyes and glared at the child.

'It's alive,' she said angrily. 'Why didn't it die? It's like him.'

I wonder why I fended Ellen off, when she tried to slap Alice? Why I told Alice she'd grow to love Margaret, who was her own child for all she looked as if she'd been badly made out of lumps of red clay? I began swaddling the baby, who bawled with hunger. Presently Alice resigned herself and put Margaret to the breast. And scolded us out of the house, as soon as we'd cleaned her. I tried to come back the next day, but she wouldn't let me in. She shut herself up with the husband she hated and the child she loathed.

She cared for Margaret, fed and clothed her. She did her duty by her. Wasn't that enough? More than enough, when she killed her husband's half-brother for Margaret.

We can let ourselves know that, now that we know all the rest.

MARGARET

I WAKE up from this dream of struggle and death, and I'm still alive, I can scarcely believe it. I never shake Thomas and tell him about it. Who'd want to listen? It's not the sort of dream folks are interested in.

CHAPTER FOURTEEN

ALICE MUMBLED: 'Ellen Cox, Judith Tegg's mother, shall I tell you what she did?'

Richard said hastily: 'Ellen is dead, Alice. Nothing can make any difference to her state, bliss or torment, she is there for ever. It is your fate hangs in the balance. I want to hear about your crimes.'

'I told her I'd catch her out one day,' said Alice.

The bell rang five times. She was still mumbling, he had to strain to hear her. My effort, he thought, what rotten fruit it has produced!

'Did you kill her?' he asked. His words struck the inside of his own head and hurt him.

'No,' she said, indistinctly. 'I didn't need to kill her.'

'Who did you need to kill? James Warren? Your husband's brother?'

Kill, he thought, kill, kill, the word loses its meaning with so much repetition.

'Oh,' Alice said loudly, 'if only I'd been able to kill all of you.'

Weakly, shrinking, he said: 'Thou shalt not kill, Alice!'

Her face was sharp with rage. 'And the gallows, Richard Berkeley, that's waiting to kill me?'

He said: 'The gallows is a different matter, Alice. The gallows will bring the killing to an end.'

She let out a fluttering, high-pitched whine of fear. He covered his face with his hands.

JAMES SYKES

THEY WEIGH everything by how much use it is for them; and so they turn needy old women away from their doors. They cannot see that a thing can be good in itself. So it is useful to them, now, to believe that Alice killed James Warren. When that story was against their interests, they closed their ears to it. Though they always looked askance at the child Simon in our midst.

Had there been witchcraft involved, I would have taken it up, and had Alice before the Church courts. No one would have been more pleased to do that. My own sad past makes me the most reliable witness. But nobody is interested in the truth, though it remains necessary even when some would say: Too late.

James Warren was Alice's brother-in-law, the son of Francis Slade's mother by an earlier marriage, and a better one. John Warren had been a sober, well set-up man who looked after his land. Michael Slade was a young good-for-nothing who used his pretty face and sweet tongue, to say nothing of what he did with his hands, to climb into Widow Warren's bed. And as soon as she'd wed with this Michael, she took against her son James. She would turn her face from him, to dote on the ugly drunken brat Francis, though to be just, his drunkenness – before he was five – was his father's fault. Michael would stop his squalls by stuffing pieces of bread soaked in ale into his toothless baby mouth. The child was a confirmed drunkard before he was twelve, and already plagued with the monstrous delusions that shortened his life. Then Thomazine died of the plague, and Francis was left alone with Michael, who died himself in an alehouse brawl when Francis was eighteen. That was when I came to the parish: I had the tale from my churchwarden, a man as unlike Robert Tarry as you might find, thin, taciturn, and given to telling the truth.

Francis did nothing to repair the waste of his property, till he married Alice, who went better to work with it.

James, meanwhile (who had been twelve when his mother remarried), had gone to stay with an uncle who was in trade in London, then left for the New World when he was a young man. But in the year I'm thinking of, he came back to the village with a certain amount of money in his pocket, and got work as a farm labourer. He was set on winning the land back from Francis: he said it was rightfully his.

SARAH

EVEN NOW I can see Alice's face: furious, savage with rage. She said to me: 'The only reason my father made me marry the sot was the land he sat on, and the money I could make with it. Now, when I've been working more than two years to mend the holding, and been saddled with his ugly fool of a child, they want to take it all away from me. And then Francis can beat us silly in the ditch. Why didn't James Warren die of fever in the New World?'

The words ring louder in my ear than all the creaks of the house or the pig's noise: they ought to prove it. They don't. There's something I missed somewhere, something I regret, not that I didn't give her unnatural pleasure—

Yet I desired that lewdness, and so I made the channel for her to harm me—

It's something harder to pin down, something that squeezes my heart when my memory brings up the picture of Alice's young desperate face.

Though all that's gone.

That day I saw she was shivering, and put my arm round her. She shook me off.

And the village was divided on the issue. You would see them talking to Alice, flattering her, asserting her rights for her. 'Where does this fellow come from?' they would ask. Then they would leave Alice, turn the corner, and meet James. 'Yes,' they would say, 'you've been wronged, that's quite clear—'

This is a small place, and no one likes to cause offence.

When they talked to neither they agreed that Ralfe had slipped up for once, giving Alice to Francis – but who else would have taken her? No one discussed it with Ralfe at all, firstly because he seldom talked to anyone except about business, and secondly because we didn't want to find ourselves covered with boils, or plagued with hordes of bedbugs. Ralfe's punishments were never too heavy, but they had their effect.

And James would meet Alice on the street, and say to her, oh, so sure of himself: 'Everyone sees the justice of my claim. If you were reasonable, you'd move out today.'

Alice would snarl her face up at him and slide away. She knew, better than he did, that no one was saying what they really thought. Though most of them preferred not to think at all. And unlike James Warren who, however hard-working and respectable he was, remained a stranger, she could sense the village's dislike of this festering squabble among us. We were angry with James, for starting it, and with Alice and Francis, for being involved in it.

JAMES SYKES

AND IF the case had come to law, there would have been no contest. The land had been left to Francis's mother, without conditions. But James seemed to want the village to decide – as if it would make good what his mother had done to him. He grew more irritable – and less popular – as he began to realise that the village would never take either side.

Alice grew thinner than ever, and worked like a dog in a treadmill. Incessantly, it appeared, she pushed food down Margaret's throat, and Margaret grew fatter than ever I've seen a child, the two of them were like a hedge-sparrow with a cuckoo-chick, and always Margaret's eyes were on Alice, her eyes that seemed to say she was starving, that however much she ate and however fat she grew, she would never be satisfied.

The hen bird was afraid of the chick – though the hedge-sparrow, in Nature, seems to be unaware that its head will be bitten off at last. Yet Alice had no reason to fear, since the true cuckoo-chick was Bridget. And so easily are we misled.

And Francis got drunk seven days a week instead of three, and beat his wife more cruelly than he had ever done. Though I detested Alice and all her works, though I believed it was the husband's right – even his duty, God help me! – to beat his wife, when Alice appeared covered in bruises and both eyes blackened, I knew it was too much. The village expected me to speak to him about it. I did so, but had to take to my heels, for he was a violent man, and had no respect for my cloth.

MARGARET

SHE NEVER asked me if I wanted food or not, she stuffed me like a force-fed goose. And told me how hungry she went, so I could eat. Every mouthful she forced on me, I was stealing from her. That was my mother.

★

RICHARD THOUGHT: The night is ebbing away, and the daybreak will make a fool of me.

'James Warren,' he shouted at Alice. 'We know it all already, but your confession may save you from hell's torment. You cannot lie to God, woman.'

I hate him, thought Alice. My hands, itching for the bare throat, my fingers reaching for the knife. These things are real. And James Warren's face, twisted with pain, the lie on his lips, the lie he hoped he could save himself with.

She wanted to speak and say: I am a killer. But her mouth was quite dry and no sound would come out.

JUDITH

WHAT MY mother told me about James Warren was that Alice had her husband set about him one night and break his arm. Knowing there was no bone-setter better than herself. Then she came to him, and pretended to help him, in exchange for his promise to give up his lawsuit. But she poisoned him with her magic, so when he came to himself again and wouldn't keep the promise she'd forced on him – and why should he? – she brought about his death.

'Keep her sweet,' said my mother. 'She knows too much about us. But if you ever have the chance to get rid of her—'

SARAH

FRANCIS HAD two drinking companions, Peter Gough and Giles Cox, and they liked to inflame him, sometimes because it was useful to them, sometimes because it amused them. Giles Cox had a cottage here, but he came and went, and when he went, we'd often hear tell of some poor folk's throat slit and all their valuables gone. Giles would come back with money in his purse. When he smiled at you, you'd watch his butcher's hands and feel for your purse. He was uncle to our virtuous and self-satisfied Judith Tegg, brother-in-law to the midwife, Ellen Cox, and a standing reproach to the family's vaunted honesty. Peter Gough had no honest relatives: he was Lisbeth Tarry's father, and how Robert expected any good to come of marriage with her – cheats, father and daughter alike. Lisbeth was a smiling cheat, and Peter was a bad-tempered cheat. If you gave Peter the time of day he'd fall out with the voice you used. When my father-in-law spoke to him about a badly made horseshoe, Peter flared up like his own furnace. He picked up a piece of red-hot iron with his tongs, and said he was a good smith, and he'd throw the iron straight through my father-in-law to prove it. That was how Peter came to be bound over to keep the peace, that was the sort of man he was. It was he who stole the Communion cup. Who else could it have been?

James Warren was set on by two ruffians one moonless night, and had his arm broken with a cudgel. He knew who'd attacked him. No doubt Francis repaid them with a night's worth of drinks and whoring. At Alice's expense. And now James Warren was in a trap, for who was the best bone-setter in the village (except Lady Berkeley, who was confined with her second son, our Vicar), but Alice?

At first James Warren had no notion of letting Alice lay hands on him, but he changed his tune after one or two women had tried and half killed him. 'I'll have her,' said he. 'I can't bear the pain any longer. I'd have the Devil, if he could help me.' I'd forgotten, till this moment, that he said that.

And Alice liked power. There was nothing else she liked so well.

JAMES SYKES

SHE CAME out of compassion – who dares to say she had none of that in her? It was not, as I then thought, only to keep her credit in the village, for fear she might lose custom if she was linked to what Francis had done.

ALICE SAID to Richard: 'I was honest, when I set his arm. He was glad to promise to give up his lawsuit. He'd have agreed to anything while he was in such pain, believing I could help him. Which I did.'

He stared at her. Liar, his eyes said, murderer, black witch.

Angrily, she said: 'It was your fault, as much as mine. If you hadn't been a new baby, your mother would have attended him. And my father, when I'd asked him for help, all he said was: 'When your opportunity comes, use it.' He didn't care much. He only ever cared about three things, money, my mother, and Juliet. My mother was dead, and money was losing its hold. Half the time, he'd send his clients on to me. He had enough, upstairs in his cottage, the moths and rats and dormice were tired of admiring those stacks of silver coins. But he never had enough of running his hands over Juliet's golden hair.' She spat.

Richard asked: 'Didn't you plan the whole thing with

your husband?' And thought: By my birth, I killed this man. I have been Alice's accomplice all my life.

Alice said: 'I'd never have planned anything with Francis. I told him to do something: he threatened to have the branks put on me to stop my tongue, and drove me and Margaret both into the pigsty to spend the night there in the frost and filth. Don't you listen to anything? It was my opportunity. James Warren thought I was sweet and fragrant, because I knew how to ease his pain, he loved me better than the land at that moment. I knew the time had come. I did it for Margaret, that ungrateful lump of lard.'

A pale film seemed to come over her eyes: she stared through it at the wall. Richard thought: We have always been here, in this dawn light, in this cell, listening to the drip of the water and her old breath panting. And her hair standing out like white frazzled hemp.

'So he healed,' said Alice, in a whining voice, 'but while he was healing, he couldn't work, and had to leave his bed in the farmhouse. He took lodgings with Widow Sharpe, and went to work in her bed. Ploughed her so well, she was with child in a month. So now there it was: "James, marry me, James, our child will need something to live on, don't keep your promise, James, take up your lawsuit, James."'

Richard asked: 'What did you do, Alice?' Against all the odds, he thought, I may yet win.

JAMES SYKES

FLUX AND change are of the nature of Creation, thus when all of us thought James Warren would be with us for ever, forever railing at the Slades but never going to law, he did two things. First, he filed his suit at last, taking most of the Widow Sharpe's money to give the lawyer as well as his own, and secondly, he fell victim to a seizure, in Widow Sharpe's bed, and inside her person.

He died three days later. He died of natural causes. I would assert that truth under torture.

JUDITH

I saw the black weasel again yesterday evening: it comes when the shadows are growing long. It looks at me with its green eyes, it smiles and shows its teeth. It knows what I hid under my sheets, against my legs, shivered with fear and the hard cold of it, when I was a child. The weasel was there, maybe, spying on me. It grows more insolent every day. Will it jump at my throat soon?

Alice said: 'I told him he'd done himself no good. I told him cheats never prosper. He laughed at me, but I knew my words had got into his blood.'

'You killed him,' said Richard. 'As you killed all the rest.'

'Yes,' said Alice.

SARAH

The Widow thought he was crying with passion, but it was as good as his death-cry. He never let out another sound. When she managed to heave him off her and out of her, she tended him for three days, begging the Parson to wed them, which our Reverend Sykes refused to do. For how could James Warren consent? He was as active as a log.

There's never been any proof that Simon was James Warren's son, though the Widow made a great show, in the early years, of exhibiting her lover's nose, his bent toes, the mole above his navel, and other things she could have kept quiet about, on the baby's body. People smiled and nodded, but anyone except Widow Sharpe might have sensed their distaste.

And she never got her money back. The lawyer gambled it away along with his own and other folk's property in two days and nights of dicing. He got up from the table and ran away to France. The Widow and her brat would have been completely destitute, had not the Parson seen to it that she got the licence for the alehouse. But that was her destruction, for she died of drink, and her son will do the same.

RICHARD said: 'And did get help from the Devil to kill James Warren, out of my fear of his claim on my husband's land.' He waited for her to repeat his words. But his brain said: You are being cruel, you have always been cruel to women, and to yourself. He felt a great cold emptiness in his belly and chest.

Alice began to whimper, to sob and gasp: 'You're taking me away from myself, you're making someone else of me, I shall never find her again, the one I was meant to be.'

'Do you hate me?' he asked.

She said: 'You are good, in your own way. But what good does that do me?'

She thought: I must be kind to them, because I have killed so many of them. If I believe what they believe, I will not be completely cast out.

'I am wicked,' she said. 'I'll say anything you want.'

The bell rang six times. The sun came out of the clouds and shone into the cell as if morning had never happened before. The gaoler came to tell them the cart was ready. He was roughly forbearing towards Alice, almost apologetic. Oh, she thought. It's beginning to work. I'll give them the confession they want, and my death will mean something.

JAMES SYKES

THERE IS a time to save, and a time to slay, a time to dance, and a time to mourn. There is a time to lose, and to know our loss. And were we all able to live so naturally, we would find God more surely than through all the prayers and conjurations of hireling ministers.

JUDITH

IT WAS my mother, Ellen Cox, who stole the cup from the church. My uncle Giles had promised he'd sell it for her, but he didn't come home the night she took it. No one suspected her: she'd been cleaning the church. She had a reputation for honesty. She stowed it under my bed, and still my uncle stayed away. Night after night we waited for him. It would have saved us from penury, bad harvests, the agony about the rent. 'We'll spend the money little by little,' said my mother. 'No one will guess.'

But Alice came, instead of my uncle: there she stood in the doorway, smiling. 'Let it be found,' she said, 'and nothing more will be said about it.' All the years of giving

Alice business, even after my mother's death! Then she began to gabble everyone's business to her bees.

My head is spinning.

The black weasel is watching, its green eyes measure my distraction. If I tell Robert Tarry, will he get me hanged?

CHAPTER FIFTEEN

MARGARET

I WASHED her old carcass as if she was my own child. She can't have known much tenderness when she was so small. Now the old woman is dead, would I be able to mother the little child? Oh, my darling, let me rock you, you're crying.

If I listen to her, she might tell me why she never said those words to me.

I think she always felt she had done something wrong. Sly, her own mother said. Ill-favoured. But Lydia looked at her elder child, Jacob, and smiled with content. She looked at Alice, and found fault with her work.

But even when she was four years old, she got good wool from her distaff. And Ralfe, her father, said one day he'd let her look in the silver bowl. He knew she had the skill.

At night her mother, Lydia, complained to her father: 'My own child's been taken from me, and I have to make do with this wizened creature! You could have stopped it, why didn't you send Alice where she belongs?'

Alice could hear those words, coming through the curtain of the bed-space where they slept. She was hungry, her stomach forever yearning. Lydia stinted her. (So she told me, excusing herself for stuffing my mouth.)

'Lydia,' said her father, 'it wouldn't have brought the other one back.'

There was weeping, in the dark.

The house was full of secrets, they were Lydia's dreams, she spun them like wool, on an invisible wheel, and the rooms were strung with them. You had to find your way round them, step over or under them, you couldn't go straight across the floor. Alice dodged and crawled, Ralfe stepped over them, Lydia pushed them up and let them drop.

But Jacob walked through them, broke them all the time, and his mother smiled, painfully this time, and offered him food. Jacob was fat. Though not as fat as his niece, big Margaret, myself.

Alice learned that the other people in the village smiled warily at Ralfe, Lydia and herself. But they laughed at Jacob. No one was afraid of Jacob, the way they were afraid of the others in the family. One day she learned that Jacob was afraid of his little sister, Alice. Then she laughed.

THE CART bumped and jolted along the road. Richard and Alice had to clutch each other to keep themselves upright. There were people all along the road: it was a special day. Murderers were hanged every day of the week, but a witch's execution was less common.

The wind caught her hair and pulled it away from her head. She thought: No, this isn't my route. I can't be going to my death. The crowd jeered and shouted insults at her, but she heard nothing because of the wind blowing in her ears. Something will happen, she thought. I'll fly away, like those crows that are playing in the gusts ahead of us. Then she understood that the crows were round the gibbet.

Richard thought: They'd pelt her, if I wasn't here. I am her protector. She needs me.

He looked at the crowd, and there were tiny winged

creatures flitting among them and alighting on their shoulders, whether batwinged or feathered, cherubs or small demons, he had no idea. The wheels hit an enormous rut, and they both staggered and fell over. The crowd roared: sweat burst out on his face. His hands went out to her, to help her up, a voice inside his brain gabbled: Mother, Susan. He stilled it, and thought: Alice. When they arrived at the gibbet, Alice wanted to wave and smile at all these people who were so glad to see her. She stopped herself in time, and took hungry gulps at the fresh air, as if she would store it up against the strangle-hold of the rope.

MARGARET

JACOB SAID to Alice: 'You know too much. You have hungry eyes.'

Lydia heard that, and she whipped Alice.

My grandmother Lydia had a dead baby born in shreds because the midwife got it out with hooks.

And Jacob told Alice: 'It's your fault. You shouldn't have looked at Mother.'

This time Lydia didn't whip Alice, because she was too feeble.

She stopped working, and it was the spiders' turn to drape the house, this time with visible grey shrouds. Once Alice heard the village women tutting at the filth, so she came home and tried to clean it up, small as she was.

But: 'Leave it be,' said her mother. Lydia smelt of blood. The family walked in hens' mess, they wore dirty clothes, they were alive with fleas and lice. Lydia's belly began to grow again.

'This time she'll die,' said the women.

Alice must have been forever listening, maybe she thought she might make sense of it all, if she listened long enough?

'She has the eaglestone,' they said. 'She won't die, with the eaglestone.'

Women come through childbirth, their baby comes away easily, if they carry that stone with the smaller one rattling inside it. This is flint country, but you don't find such things easily, even here.

My grown mother had one, who was small Alice. The child I'm carrying inside me now, so I can rattle her loose.

AT THE gallows, Alice demanded of herself: 'Did I hide it? Did I?'

'Hide what?' asked Richard Berkeley, worried by the interruption to a confession which had, so far, been exemplary.

MARGARET

THE EAGLESTONE means safety, and small Alice must have wanted safety. And maybe, also, that stone.

ONE FOOT on the ladder, Alice cried: 'Where is there a place for me to say that I loved Bridget, I loved Juliet, I loved my mother, and I tried to love my daughter?'

The crowd had not come to hear such words, so they shivered in the biting wind, and forgot them.

MARGARET

So she was lonely, and They came to her, with their wicked laughter and bright clothes. They traced patterns inside her closed eyelids at night, They told her stories when she lay in bed. She shared the stories with pretty little Sarah and Sarah wailed and laughed for fear, and clung to Alice.

It was They, the Good Folk, who told her to piss in the ale she had to fetch for Jacob. They taught her how to twist free of his hold on her wrists. They said: 'You belong to us, you are our child, we won't leave you alone.' She'd escape to them, in the woods, feast on berries and the toadstools They'd told her were safe to eat, and shiver for delight in the warm rain.

The dog howled for a death, every night. Coffin-shaped embers fell out of the fire by the score. Lydia had lost the eaglestone.

'Alice,' asked Sarah, 'why are you pulling the petals off the daisy?'

'So see if you'll love me, when we're grown up.'

'Don't be a fool, a woman can't love a woman.' Alice laughed.

Oh, I know, I have to know, even if it means listening at doors and putting my ear to cracks. Even if the things I hear and see hurt me.

But this time, Alice was thinking: I want her to live, I want her to die, I want her to live, I want her to die . . .

'Alice, what's that hidden in your pouch?'

'Nothing.'

Sarah kissed Alice. Sarah shared food with her, in return for which Alice helped Sarah spin, feed the chickens, gather eggs. And enticed the Good Folk round to give Sarah's house an extra scouring. Sarah was pretty, teasing, sometimes she pushed Alice away, even slapped her. But always came back, all smiles, as if nothing had happened.

Jacob used to ambush Alice in her bed: first thing in the morning, he'd press his hands down over her mouth, let go, tweak her little nipples so the pain ran all over her, stick his fingers up her nose, press his thumbs into her eyes—

'You mustn't wake Mother,' said he, pious as a parson. 'It'd kill her.'

She asked Them for help: They danced and wriggled and told her more stories. When she told those stories to Jacob he wailed and blubbered with fear. He could never be sure she wasn't making the tales up.

'Alice, there isn't a Thing in the well, is there? I'll kill you when I catch you.'

As with all her stories, she came to believe it herself, so she kept telling it. Now the villagers keep away from the well at new moon. There's no more a bloodsucking goblin down there than there's Noll Cromwell with all his horses and guns.

They lived on cheese and bread, like labourers – nobody cooked. And the land went the way of the house. When Ralfe made his hay, he forgot to vent it properly and the whole stack burned down, while Ralfe stood watching with a faint smile on his face. They remember that smile to this day, in the village, though everyone who saw it is dead.

Then one of the cows began to piss blood, and Ralfe, who knew better than anyone else how to treat it, did nothing, left it with the others, and all four of them took the disease and died. In spite of this – or maybe because of it – more and more people came to consult Ralfe; the crazier he got, the better at his work. So they could buy as much bread and cheese as they needed.

Ralfe hardly ever said a word to either of his children.

The hens' eggs were left to go rotten – none of the hens went broody or made a nest. But Lydia brooded. She grew paler every day, and filled up with water, in her hands, in her legs, about her face. She was monstrous to look at.

And the ghostly hunter came out of the forest with his hounds and hunted right up against the wall of the house.

Ralfe began to teach his trade to Alice. She had to learn how and when to pick herbs, how to use the silver bowl, the shears, and the sieve for divination. She was best with the silver bowl. Now at least one of her parents was talking to her, though only when she was being taught. As soon as the lesson ended Ralfe's mouth shut up like a locked chest.

Alice was afraid, I think, but since she was Alice she couldn't tell anyone, so she frightened other people instead.

'You see that weasel?' she asked Sarah, while Jacob hung about, pretending to listen. Alice looked at him sidelong with her green eyes. 'That's a woman who insulted the fairies. So they turned her into a weasel, but if she could only drink her baby's blood she'd be a woman again. Then they'd hang her on the gibbet, so she has to stay the way she is, hunt mice and rabbits and drink their blood, while what she really wants is to have her own baby by the throat, I saw it in her eyes, she's so thirsty for that blood that would make her a woman again, but she doesn't want to hang on the gibbet.'

That's another story they tell, in Whitchurch, as if it were the truth. My mother left the village with more ghosts than she found it with – and most of them never died.

Sarah was sick. Alice laughed till the tears ran, clutching her stomach.

But Sarah screamed in her sleep all that night – her mother decided she was bewitched, so who better to consult than Ralfe? Ralfe looked in his own bowl and found the witch's face: his daughter's. It was when he saw her reflection that he noticed, for the first time, how pinched Alice's face was, the way her green eyes looked as if they were just about to pop out of it, the way her hair stuck out like untidy russet straw.

Ralfe told Sarah's mother she must have gone too near a fairy ring. He gave her a charm to tie on Sarah's wrist, and ordered Alice to comb her hair, and eat more. But took no steps to watch how much food she took. And Alice's stories dried up – till the charm was snatched off by a bramble when Sarah was picking blackberries. But by then, everything had changed.

Now Jacob looked round the kitchen. He saw cobwebs and mouldering crusts and cheese-rinds lying about. He saw rats and mice running in and out while the cat looked on and smiled. He saw filthy dishes used again and again without washing. He trod on an egg and wailed at the stinking mess on his shoe.

He stood in the middle of the house, hating the want of order, then he went to work. He gathered up all the eggs he could find, threw the dustiest away outside the house, and set off to town to sell the cleanest at market. He was hardly out of the village when there was a pecking inside one of the shells, and a chick popped out and lay on top of the basket, its feathers lying any way, dying in the fresh air. Jacob tossed the thing out and hurried on to town, but now he kept a fearful eye on the rest of the eggs in the basket.

When he got to town the hawkers were packing up their baskets; he hadn't known to set out early, and there was no one left to sell anything to.

'Sell 'em from door to door,' said an old woman kindly. He had a pretty face.

But he had that vice that's been my downfall, too – being, perhaps, so stupid it had to be so. Honesty. It tripped him up. When the first housewife opened up to him what did he say to her, but that he had rotten eggs to sell? She laughed at him, then shooed him away from the door: 'Stop wasting my time,' she said, 'if I want rotten eggs I can get them at the pillory, and throw them at you.' She slammed the door, and he ran away with tears pouring down his face. Poor fool.

Two eggs fell out of the basket and smashed on his feet. Inside one was a half-formed chick, the other – for a wonder – was fresh. He smashed every egg in the basket, there and then in the gutter. If they weren't rotten, there was a chick growing inside, or else full-grown and rotting away again. Jacob thought it was his mother's doing, she was brooding the chicks inside the eggs no hen came near, then letting them die before they could hatch. So the chick had hatched when he took the egg away from Lydia's house. And he bawled. He understood what a fool he was, and how little chance there was that anything good would ever come of him. Or so I think. And the story about him selling rotten eggs, they tell it in the town to this day.

The next thing he knew he was running away, and had got to the edge of the forest – so I once heard my mother telling Bridget – ashamed to go home.

She said Ralfe could see him all the time, reflected in his silver bowl. Amazed at his son's idiocy, which was richer than anyone had yet thought. By and by Jacob walked into the forest and lost himself there. When Ralfe saw the night-spirits in the trees, talking about what they'd do to Jacob, he must have wondered if he should set off to find his son, but he'd got out of the habit of caring, so he turned away from the bowl and left them all to it.

A jack-o'-lantern, said my mother, led him into a bog, his feet stuck fast and he stayed there half the night, shivering and struggling and scared even more witless than he was already. When he managed to get his feet loose, the marsh gas came up in great bubbles and laughed at him. He found a hollow tree to spend the rest of the night, but the boggarts and spooks came after him, and breathed down the back of his neck. Anger brewed in him and filled his empty head.

He came limping home the next day. Alice laughed at his tears and the mud smeared all over him. And then he thought he'd be really cunning, hugged himself for pleasure at the only cleverness in his life. Which he used to destroy himself.

'Alice,' he said, 'there are trout in the millstream, but I can't find them, come and find them for me, I'll hook them, and we'll cook the fish and eat it together. Please, Alice,' he said, 'I've been bad to you, I'll love you for ever if you do that.'

His head had confused Alice's stories with the real fright he'd had, so he thought Alice had lost him in the forest. And maybe he remembered a little sister who'd been beloved and plump and smiling – till wizened squalling Alice had taken her place. Alice, for her part, was starving for more than hot fish. Ralfe watched them go, and noticed a darkness about their heads – but he did nothing.

Poor children. That's what I'm thinking. Poor children. All of them, Jacob, Alice, Juliet, Margaret, Bridget.

They walked along the path and the dust flew up round them like flour. The birds were asleep, you could only hear the insects buzzing. It had turned into a hot, hot day. They'd never have caught the trout, who were dozing in the deep shadows.

And maybe Jacob would have pushed Alice in, as he intended. But Alice trod on an overhanging piece of the bank, and tumbled splash and shriek into the water.

You think you're hating someone, all of a sudden you're loving them instead. Jacob jumped in to save her, he didn't even take his shoes off first, and forgot he couldn't swim.

They slid, both of them, into the water, both of them had to fight and struggle and felt their chests squeezed for want of air. But Alice let herself go, and the water bore her up, pushed her to the bank, and let her climb out. It wouldn't have her, they say now.

It wanted Jacob: his second baptism took him straight to heaven.

They found Jacob's body when it had blown up enough to make it float. Alice never even caught a chill. The same night Jacob was hooked out of the river, Lydia gave birth to her live daughter Juliet, and died herself, lacking the eaglestone. And Alice screamed and sobbed and tore her hair out. Poor lonely child.

EPILOGUE

BUT THE same Alice did make a most edifying End on
the Scaffold, and did Confess to All she had Done, and
confessed she had long Deserved this Fate, and wondered
how God had permitted her to do the Devill's work for
so long, and did crave mercy for her Soule, recognising
that her Body must Dye. Then did she climb the Ladder,
and the Executioner after her, and was turned off. And
did Dye within Half an Houre or so, and was taken down,
being dead.

RICHARD

THE AIR was so sweet, coming out of the stink of the
gaol! Reminding me that there is life, given us by God,
our duty to live it, though the world may have crashed in
pieces around us. My wife is dead: I must be good to my
daughters.

Today I planted the second yew-sapling in the churchyard. I did it myself, in my shirt-sleeves, dug the thin soil
down to the stubborn earth beneath, flints and clay, flints
and clay. My spade jarred my arm. And I thought: Alice
lies in this churchyard, in spite of me. I thought it with
pleasure. What is becoming of me? The villagers judged
me crazy. Perhaps I am. Another mad parson for this

village. Only I shall not leave, as Sykes did. I shall remain, die, and be buried here. There have been vicars of St Leonard's for four hundred years, and I am the latest of them. That is enough.

I have sweated the gaol-stench out of me.

THREE RIPE apples have fallen out of the tree. Shall we pick them up? They are red, tender-skinned, and their flesh is tinged pink and sweet: they are the kind of apples that will not keep, but eat them new, they are the fruit of paradise.

One is for me, to wet my mouth after telling the story – and I ask pardon for any imperfections in my fantasy – the second is for you who have shared them with me, and the third is for Margaret, who says: 'I am free now.' And goes on her way.